FEMALE FITNESS ON FOOT

Walking, Jogging, Running, Orienteering

Bob O'Connor, Eystein Enoksen,
Christine Wells and Eldin Onsgard

Wish Publishing
Terre Haute, Indiana
www.wishpublishing.com

Edited by Kim Heusel
Proofread by Christopher Stolle
Cover designed by Phil Velikan
Cover photo by Corbis Images
Interior photography by Bob O'Connor

Printed in the United States of America
10 9 8 7 6 5 4 3 2 1

Published in the United States by
Wish Publishing
P.O. Box 10337
Terre Haute, IN 47801
www.wishpublishing.com

Distributed in the United States by
Cardinal Publishers Group
7301 Georgetown Road, Suite 118
Indianapolis, IN 46268
www.cardinalpub.com

PREFACE

Almost without question, the most popular fitness programs involve walking, jogging, running or any combination of the three. While these activities are inexpensive, the highly effective aerobic benefits they provide can prove invaluable. No expensive equipment or special facilities are needed, but as simple as walking, jogging or running might be, there are ways to make the exercise more effective, enjoyable and safer.

As you become more adept at walking, jogging or running, you might want to try some competition. You can learn Olympic walking, enter 5- or 10-kilometer races or begin orienteering — something like a treasure-hunting race. Orienteering is one of the fastest growing sports for those who like to challenge their brains along with conditioning their bodies.

This book is designed to introduce the beginner to walking, jogging and running and help you understand why you should begin a lifelong program. How to do it effectively and how to wisely purchase the equipment you might need are also covered. If you are already seriously into fitness, this book provides more advanced information that is useful in training and in competition. The chapters on running biomechanics, sprinting, conditioning for competition, overtraining and developing strength are included for those who are more advanced and competitive.

Whether you walk or run, proper nutrition and maintaining good health are also important, so we will take a look at the latest information on effective eating as well as safety and injury prevention. Modern studies have shown that some of the warmup techniques that we have always used are actually harmful. We cite a number of scientific studies to prove the points we make — because the research often indicates that what is commonly believed is wrong.

Hopefully, this book will serve as a guide on how to develop walking and running into a more effective body conditioner and, above all, set up an exercise pattern that you can enjoy throughout your life.

TABLE OF CONTENTS

1

INTRODUCTION

The doctors and philosophers of ancient Greece and the medical researchers of today agree on the values of exercise. Thomas Jefferson said that walking was the best of all exercises. Today, we realize that both walking and running can help us reclaim benefits that our sedentary lives have stolen away.

The greatest health needs in our modern world are to exercise and to control our weight. The two go hand in hand. The overweight problem, which first seemed to materialize in the United States, is now evident in much of the Western world. Britain started from a lower base but has followed the same path as the United States. Australia has now equaled the United States with about 55 percent of its people overweight or obese. Even in the underdeveloped countries, obesity is increasing. The World Health Organization predicts an increase of 50 million obese people in the next 25 years with an attendant doubling of diabetes to 300 million people. The lack of exercise causes most of the overweight problems we observe. This is a major reason that so many people have undertaken walking or running programs.

WALKING AND RUNNING FOR FITNESS

Walking and running are the oldest forms of human locomotion. They are also the most popular approach to fitness today. You can achieve fitness on foot on any road or path, on treadmills in a health studio and in various types of competition. Whether you want to exercise alone or with others, in a noncompetitive mode or in competition, on a road or in the woods, there is a type of fitness with which you can be content.

We will look at the correct form for walking, jogging, distance running and sprinting. We will look at how you can join in orienteering, a popular worldwide activity that combines map reading and running in the woods in a competitive setting. While just recently becoming popular in the United States, it is enjoyed in more than 75 other countries. We will look at ways to improve your health and fitness through nutrition and special conditioning.

HISTORY

Running has been an important skill in the daily life of humankind for thousands of years. Carrying messages over great distances, particularly during war, has been common. In ancient wars, delivering messages on foot was essential; today, countless electronic devices now handle the job with which fleet runners were at one time entrusted. So, now we run for the joy of running and the health benefits that it develops.

In the ancient games in Athens, which were held to honor the gods, the competitors ran the sprint distances of one stadium (177 to 210 meters) and two stadiums (354 to 420 meters). The stadium length varied from one place to another. In Olympia, it was 192.27 meters; in Delphi, 177.5 meters; in Epidauros, 181.3 meters; and in Pergamon, 210 meters. One stadium was the only event that was performed during the first 13 years after the start of the ancient Greek games in 776 B.C. When running the two-stadium distance, the competitors had to run around a stake or a statue made of stone as the turning point.

The stadium at Rhodes is a good example of an ancient stadium used in ancient Greek athletics.

Everyone has heard of Greek runner Pheidippides, who ran from Marathon to Athens to tell the Athenians of the Greek victory over the Persians. (His real name was Philippides, but historical texts corrupted his name.) That was in 490 B.C. A greater exploit was runner Mensen Ernst, who brought official messages for the government from Moscow to Constantinople — a distance of nearly 1,500 miles.

The story behind the marathon race is related to the run of Pheidippides, who, after running more than 20 miles, announced that "we won the battle," then fell dead. The decision to make an Olympic event of the run from Marathon to Athens was in honor of that warrior's feat. This marathon distance was run for the first time in the first Olympic games in Athens in 1896 and in the last world championship in track and field in Athens in the summer of 1997. The length of the first competition was 40 km. In 1921, the International Track and Field Federation decided that the length of the marathon race would to be standardized at 26 miles and 385 yards (42,195 meters).

Nearly every society plays games and holds contests, and running has always played an important role in competition.

SOME ADVANTAGES OF FITNESS

Aerobic fitness is the best method of improving our immune systems, thereby increasing our resistance to infectious diseases such as colds. It strengthens our hearts and breathing muscles, reducing chances for heart attacks, the major cause of death in the civilized world. The risk for many cancers is

The ancient Greeks idealized running as shown on the artwork on the above vase.

also reduced, as is the chance for developing diabetes, a rapidly increasing degenerative disease. Aerobic exercise also improves our moods and reduces the effects of stress and depression. So, it has been shown that walking and running not only make significant contributions to the number of years we live but also to the quality of those years.

Aerobic exercise will also give us more energy. People who are fatigued usually want to rest, but they would be much better served if they began walking or running. Our bodies respond to the challenge of exercise. No matter when we start, the effects will be felt. Many people in their 60s and 70s, and even some in their 80s, have taken up running and are soon running 10-kilomoter races. Larry Lewis of San Francisco ran several miles daily when he was over 100.

PREVENT POTENTIAL PROBLEMS

Women have both strengths and weaknesses when it comes to endurance types of activities. On one hand, fat stores make it possible for women to continue exercising for long periods of time. On the other hand, the angle of the bones at the knee joint set women up for knee injuries, particularly in sports such as volleyball and basketball. This can also be a problem for some runners. The "female athlete triangle" (eating disorders, lack of menstruation, reduced bone density) must be a concern for high-level endurance athletes, but it is not a factor for the average exercising woman. While women might handle cold better than men, women are not always able to handle heat as well. Therefore, women must be aware of when and how to exercise in the heat.

DEVELOPING YOUR OWN FITNESS PROGRAM

The best aerobic fitness programs are cross-country skiing, swimming, walking or running. Snow and warm water might not always be abundant, but roads, sidewalks, trails and paths are always just a few feet away. Therefore, walking, jogging or running are the most readily available of the highly effective aerobic fitness methods.

So, if you are going to walk, jog or run, you will want to know how to do it safely. You will want to buy shoes that offer your feet the most comfort and that will aid in the efficient functioning of your feet. You will want to know the most efficient methods of walking or running. You will want to know how to develop a fitness program that will give you optimal results. You will want to know the best methods for effective and healthy eating. These are the things this book is designed to assist you in doing.

START WITH A PHYSICAL EXAMINATION

It is always wise to have a physical examination before starting any new exercise program. When you are young, an exam every few years is fine, but as you get older, exams every one or two years are advisable. The doctor will check your blood pressure and whether your heart beats normally. A check of leg and foot alignment would also be wise. This can give you an idea of the factors you might consider when buying walking or running shoes.

Women who have had eating disorders or a lack of menstruation might have lost some bone density. This reduction of bone strength can make these women more susceptible to bone injuries such as stress fractures, according to studies at Stanford University.[1]

If you are young, it is wise to have a complete physical with an electrocardiogram and blood work. You will probably be just fine, but the exam might point out some problem or potential problem that could cause problems later. Even if everything is normal, having the exam when you are young provides a baseline to which doctors can compare future exams later in your life.

DEFINE YOUR GOALS

You must have goals or you wouldn't be exercising. But what are those goals? Do you want to get fit, lose weight or compete in the Olympics? Whatever your goals, keep them in mind when you set up your fitness program. It is a good idea to write down your long-term goals; then, write intermediate and short-term goals. As you begin to exercise, you can see whether you are accomplishing what you want. Do you want to walk 10 miles a week? Do you want to be able to compete in a 10-kilometer run within six months? Look at your progress and evaluate your workouts.

Date	Resting pulse	My mood	Workout comments	Distance(s)	Time(s)	Pulse rate
Monday						
Tueday.						
Wednesday						
Thursday						
Friday						
Saturday						
Sunday						

RECORD YOUR PROGRESS

It is wise to record your progress each workout day. Check your resting pulse in the morning while still in bed. If you are walking or running just one distance, note the time for the run and your ending pulse rate. If you are doing multiple runs for a competitive workout, record those too (see sample chart above).

The benefits of endurance exercise include:
- An increase in the number of blood vessels. When this occurs in the heart, it increases the chances of avoiding or surviving a heart attack.
- Control of body fat. One-half hour of proper daily exercise will keep off (or take off) 26 pounds per year.
- An increase in the basal metabolism for several hours after exercising. This will take off additional pounds.
- An increase in the HDL (good cholesterol).

- A strengthening of the diaphragm, the major muscle used in breathing.
- Increased flexibility in the joints.
- An improved immunity system to fight off communicable diseases and cancer.
- Stronger bones and connective tissue.
- A reduction in minor aches, pains, stiffness and soreness.
- A reduction in chronic fatigue.
- An increased ability to relax and to sleep well.
- An increase in endorphins in the brain (if the exercise is sufficiently long), making one feel exhilarated.
- Improved digestion and bowel function.
- Increased mental capabilities due to an increase in oxygen to the brain and a decrease in stress. An increase in stamina.
- Better work records on the job.
- Increased life expectancy.

An Arabian proverb states: "He who has health has hope, and he who has hope has everything."

Notes

1. Fredericson, M. "Common injuries in runners. Diagnosis, rehabilitation and prevention."*Sports Medicine*, 21:1 (1996): 49-72.

2
EQUIPMENT

Your feet are your main concern when you indulge in fitness on foot. There are special shoes for each type of bipedal movement. Improper or worn-out shoes can stress not only your feet but also your ankles, shins, knees and hips. They can also change your stride and make it less efficient.

Shoes don't last forever. In fact, they generally lose their shock-absorbing capacities long before the soles and heels are worn away. It is suggested that you replace your shoes after 400 to 500 miles of training. If the insides of the shoes begin to break down early, replace the shoes sooner.

In days past, people ran in tennis shoes. Now that we have learned more about feet, walking and running biomechanics (mechanics of the body — how the body moves) and running stresses, shoes have been developed to meet nearly everyone's needs. If you are serious in your training methods, you will probably need specific types of shoes for indoor or outdoor workouts, for training or for competition, for working out in a weight room or for exercising on hard or soft surfaces.

SELECTING THE PROPER SHOES

When selecting shoes, you will likely hear some anatomical terms that you should know. When referring to the ankles, turning the sole of your foot inward is called *inversion*; turning them outward is called *eversion*. While not technically correct, common usage often refers to eversion as *pronation* of the ankle or the foot and inversion as *supination* of the ankle or foot. However, some researchers have called it pronation when the toes are turned outward (abduction) and the inside of the foot has rotated down (eversion). On the other hand, it is often called supination when the toes are turned inward (adduction) and the inside of the foot is turned upward (inversion).[1] Understanding these various movements of your feet is important when considering shoes or orthotics for running.

Shoes are made for many different feet and the various biomechanics that come with them — feet that turn in or out when they meet the ground,

7

shin bones or knees that twist inward or stay straight and feet that might have suffered a previous injury. It is not enough to buy shoes for walking or jogging; those shoes must fit your feet. They need to provide proper cushioning and should be of a construction that prevents blisters or other foot problems. Your budget, of course, might limit the options. Many good shoes have a price range beginning at about $70; some can be purchased for less when on sale in the shops or from Internet merchants.

As a walker or runner, your feet and legs need support where most other people do not. If your feet pronate (turn downward to the inside) you would need a shoe constructed to reduce such movement. (Overpronation is a major cause of running injuries, so your shoes should aid in injury reduction.) If your feet have very high arches, you might need a shoe designed to support your arches. Failure to support the arch can place great strain on the ligaments in your feet that hold the bones in that higher arch. Extra-wide feet must also be considered. Also, make note of the way you run — whether the heel or forefoot lands first.

Your exercise program will also determine the types of shoes you will need. If your routine is to walk some days and jog on others, you should have appropriate shoes for each activity. Walkers land on the heels on every step. Eighty-five percent of runners are also heel strikers, so cushioning and heel stability are important considerations when choosing walking and most running shoes. A walker's shoe also must be more flexible than a runner's because the walker's foot flexes on the pushoff nearly twice as much as a runner's foot does. (You might want to find a copy of the next March or April issue of *Runner's World*. A review of the newest shoes is usually presented in one of the spring issues.)

A great deal of research goes into developing sport and running shoes. Nike, for example, has more than 500 people employed in research and development. Nike, as do other major shoe companies, studies every aspect of running necessities, from materials and construction to shock absorption, stiffness, comfort, support and injury prevention. Gone are the days when men's shoes were merely narrowed or made shorter for women and children. Each gender, each age and each athletic activity requires different types of shoe constructions.

Athletic shoe stores, particularly those that specialize in walking and running shoes, are generally the best places to shop for your shoes. Some have special machines that measure your stride and the biomechanics of your foot movement. The measurements are used to help you find the best shoe for your needs. It is best to shop at several specialty stores to learn about the various shoes and what they can and cannot do for you. Shop during the middle of the day when your feet have expanded. They are slightly larger in the afternoon but might reduce again in size as evening approaches.

CHECKLIST FOR BUYING WALKING SHOES

1. Make certain the shoe is flexible for the push-off phase of the walking stride.
2. Make sure that the heel cup is sufficiently firm and strong.
3. Check for adequate cushioning under the heel.
4. The heel should be sufficiently wide. Runners' shoes often have a narrower heel.
5. Because walkers move only forward, they do not need the lateral support found in court shoes such as tennis shoes.
6. There should be plenty of room in the toe area. The toes must not be cramped.
7. Check for the *breatheability* of the upper part of the front of the shoe.
8. Check *Walking Magazine* for its annual evaluation of new walking shoes.
9. Cheap shoes will probably break down quickly, so they might be a waste of money.
10. If you have special needs, buy a special shoe.
  a. If you are race walking, buy a shoe for the activity (flatter sole andlighter weight).
  b. If you are walking in nature, over hills and down the dales, a high-top shoe with better traction should be considered.
11. Try shoes in your normal size and shoes a half-size larger to ensure proper fit.
12. If you are going to walk at night or in fog, be sure that your shoes have a reflective material in the heel area.

Have each foot measured separately. It is quite common to have feet of unequal measurements, in length and in width. When you try on the shoes, walk or run on a harder surface, not the carpeted flooring. You will want to test the cushioning qualities of the shoes.

SHOE CONSTRUCTION

Shoe construction varies with models and with manufacturers. Shoes are made with various amounts of flexibility or stiffness, with different shock-absorbing capacities, with high- or low-heel counters and with varying widths. Each of these can be important to you depending on your feet, the type of running or walking you will do and the surfaces on which you will run.

The shoe is constructed on a *last*. The last is shaped somewhat like a foot. The term *lasting* can mean a couple of things when purchasing run-

---

CHECKLIST FOR BUYING RUNNING SHOES

1. The back of the shoe should be high enough to support the heel cord — Achilles-tendon. This Achilles-tendon pad might relieve tension on the tendon, but with some runners, it increases the stress on the tendon by pushing in on it. So, for some, it is not recommended.
2. The heel should be wide enough for comfort.
3. The heel should be elevated.
4. The toe box must be wide enough for your feet.
5. Check the shock-absorbing capacities of both the sole and the heel.
6. Is the sole sufficiently durable and is the traction capability appropriate for the type of surface on which you will run?
7. Is the inner sole and heel shock absorbent?
8. Is the heel counter firm?
9. Is there an arch support?
10. Are there any inside seams that might cause blisters?
11. Does the upper allow for the release of heat through mesh or other construction?
12. If you are going to run in the evening or in fog, be sure that your shoes have a reflective material in the heel area.
13. When trying on a shoe, check that its length is about one thumb width from the end of your toes to the end of the shoe.

---

ning or walking shoes. It can mean how the bottom is shaped — straight or rounded so that it is like a rocker. A *straight-lasted* shoe is flat from the middle of the toe to the middle of the heel. This shoe will help to resist ankle pronation and should be used by sprinters who need such control. The *curve-lasted* shoe benefits those who need more foot movement and shock absorption. Walkers and most runners prefer the curved last.

The second meaning of the term lasting is used to indicate the amount of stiffness built into the lower part of the shoe. A board-lasted shoe has stiff material, such as fiberglass, inserted above the midsole. This makes the shoe reasonably stiff throughout the bottom. This type of construction is not used as much anymore. It would be used for runners or walkers who had excessive pronation during the weight-bearing part of the stride.[2]

The *board-lasted* shoe might be preferable for people who overpronate their feet (the inside of the foot rolling inward, absorbing more of the body's weight) or who are flat-footed. If you tend to wear out your shoes on the inside of the sole and heel, overpronation might be your problem. Many walkers prefer a stiffer shoe because a great deal of flexibility in the shoe might cause the muscles to tire. For runners or walkers, the

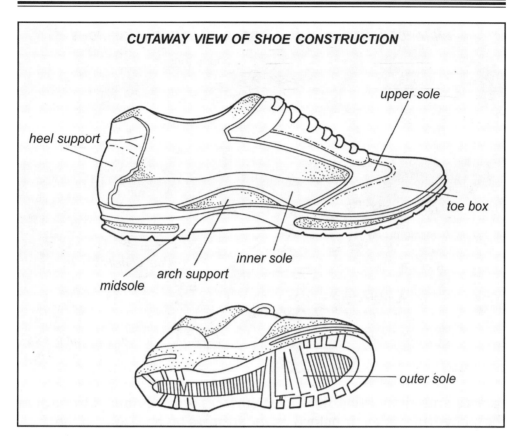

CUTAWAY VIEW OF SHOE CONSTRUCTION

upper sole

heel support

toe box

inner sole

arch support

midsole

outer sole

stiffer the sole, the less compression the heel experiences because the force of the impact of the foot strike is transferred forward more quickly.[3]

A *slip-lasted* shoe is very flexible. It achieves this flexibility by having the upper section of the shoe stitched directly to the midsole without a tougher insert between them.

A popular combination of the two methods of lasting is called the *combination last*. It is flexible (slip-lasted) in the front but stiffer (board-lasted) at the rear part of the foot.

The slip last and combination last are the more popular methods of shoe construction for running shoes today. People whose feet supinate (the bottom of the foot rolls to the inside), those with rigid feet or those with high longitudinal arches generally prefer these types of shoes.

Whenever you walk or run, a certain amount of pronation is desirable in order to disseminate the energy of the footstrike from the heel to the front of the foot (forefoot). If there is too little pronation, too much of the impact force goes to the heel and the rear part of the foot. Pronation of the foot as you transfer pressure from your heel to your big toe aids in the absorption of force two to three times your body weight as your heel hits. The downward rotation of the foot also helps in maintaining your

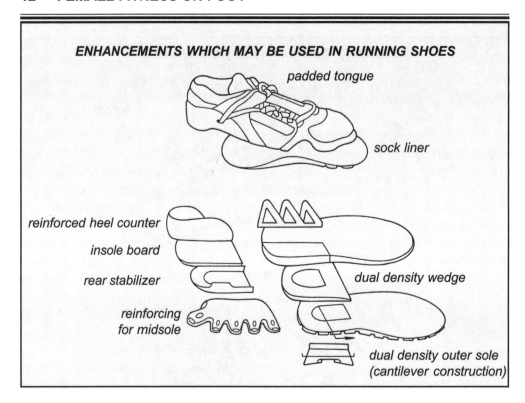

ENHANCEMENTS WHICH MAY BE USED IN RUNNING SHOES

padded tongue

sock liner

reinforced heel counter

insole board

rear stabilizer

reinforcing for midsole

dual density wedge

dual density outer sole (cantilever construction)

balance and in adjusting to uneven surfaces when running. Control of the foot when landing is helped by the stiffness of the lasting of the shoe.

The upper part of the shoe is the first thing you will see. Check for ventilation. Most running shoes are made with a mesh weave that allows for ventilation. This helps the feet to cool and reduces sweat buildup. Leather or suede is often used to bind the mesh to the sole of the shoe. Leather is stronger than the mesh, so it should help your shoes last longer. Some walkers prefer all-leather uppers. Be sure that there are enough holes in the leather to allow for ventilation. The more you perspire, the more ventilation you will need.

The job of the heel counter is to reduce ankle pronation, the inward and downward rotation of the foot. It can also spread the force of impact on landing over a greater area of the heel. You should choose a firm heel counter if you want to limit ankle pronation while running. Squeeze the heel cup firmly to see if it collapses.

An Achilles-tendon pad might extend upward from the heel. It is there to cushion the tendon, but some runners find it irritating. If you are irritated by it, cut it off or buy shoes without the pad. A higher heel might reduce the tension on the Achilles' tendon for some runners. The heel lift might be built into the shoe or added as an insert in or under the inner sole. However, not all runners will notice a reduction in tension.[4] The higher heel lift does not seem to increase the foot's pronation.

The toe box needs to have enough room to allow the toes to wiggle. A wider foot obviously needs a wider toe box. Some shoes are manufactured with a narrow toe box; others with wider toe boxes. If your feet tend to slide forward in your shoes or if you have thick toes, buy a shoe with a high toe box.

An inner sole, on which your foot will rest, will be made of a cushioning and non slipping material. Soft sponge rubber does not give enough cushioning effect, so is not recommended. You might need to buy special anti-shearing insoles if your feet tend to blister because of forward and backward movement in the shoe.

The inner sole might also have an arch support. An arch support can also be built into the next layer down in the shoe. The arch support helps reduce overpronation. If the shoe does not have all of the features you want, you might be able to add them to the shoe. (See orthotics and heel cup below.) The inner sole should be removable so that it can air out and dry between workouts.

The midsole is the next layer down and will contain most of the cushioning material of the shoe. The midsole has many functions. First, it must absorb the shock of the landing whether the footstrike is on the front of the foot (forefoot strike) or on the heel (heel strike). Heavier cushioning of the running shoes, which helps to reduce stress damage in the feet and legs, adds weight to the shoes. This reduces the running economy. Second, the midsole must be strong enough to resist inward rotation of the ankle (pronation) during the support phase, and third, it should have adequate flexibility to assist in the extension of the ankle joint.

The midsole of the shoe at the heel is flared outward from foot to ground. This flare on the inside of the shoe helps to resist ankle pronation, while the flare on the outside probably increases ankle pronation (lever force) in the landing. The medial heel flare, at the back end of the sole, helps the runner who needs to control her ankle pronation. The side (lateral) flare might be harmful to some runners, particularly if the flare is exaggerated. Researchers have found an increased number of iliotibial band friction syndrome problems. These problems are related to injury to connective tissue on the outside of the knee. The lateral flare of the heel initially slows the foot's pronation but then increases the speed of pronation. The increased speed of the pronation might be more harmful than the total pronation because the structures of the foot and leg have to adjust more quickly to the force.[5]

The bottom of the shoe has several functions. Primarily, it cushions the shock of the weight transfer, but it also makes the forward transfer of the weight from heel to toe more effective. The type and thickness of the

CHECKLIST FOR FOOT EVALUATION
1. Do you have corns, blisters, bunions, calluses or ingrown toenails? Each of these can affect the type of shoe you buy. Be sure that your new shoe does not increase the problem
2. Are your toes poorly formed — hammer toes, deflected toes inward or outward?
3. Is the long arch of the foot (longitudinal arch) low (flat foot) or very high?
4. Is the metatarsal arch (under and behind the ball of the foot) high or low?
5. Do your feet naturally turn out or in? Most people's feet turn out, but it is best if the feet point directly ahead.
6. Do your feet pronate (drop inward) or supinate (roll outward)?
Each factor can be compensated for with proper orthotics and the right shoes.

tread you will need depends on where you are going to walk or run. Exercising in the woods or running on grass will require better traction than running on a road. The type and thickness of the sole can also add to the cushioning ability of the shoe.

TRYING ON THE SHOE

Check for springiness when trying a shoe on. Those who require shock absorption in their running shoes because their lower limbs are rigid should choose shoes with soft midsoles, while those who have more mobile feet should look for a harder midsole. By using stored energy, a good rubbery midsole helps to transfer downward and backward force into an upward and forward force. While the amount of stored energy is small — usually less than one percent of the energy you need for your next step — it adds up if you are taking hundreds of steps in your workout.

The inner sole, middle sole or heel wedge might be made to absorb extra shock. This is particularly important for people who tend to get heel or stone bruises. Don't worry about shoe style; look for effective functioning. And remember, effective midsoles are especially important for women because they land with more force per pound of body weight than men.

CONTROL OF PRONATION

The control of pronation is a major factor in reducing injuries. Running barefoot actually reduces the amount of foot and ankle pronation. Consequently, exercising barefoot on grass or sand might reduce your injury potential.[6] Stiff soles, on the other hand, can increase pronation. However, they will reduce the torsion of the foot.[7] As a result, it has been suggested that the best shoe for most runners would have no heel flare, a hard midsole and a heel stabilizer.

OTHER FOOT AIDS

Orthotics are shoe inserts that generally affect the heel and both arches of the foot. Properly designed, they reduce foot, ankle and lower-leg problems. They are valuable in preventing or healing plantar fasciitis, shin splints, fallen or weak arches and a number of other problems. Runners have often found them to be helpful in holding the foot in its proper position and in making their shoes fit more effectively.

In running, there is the pronation of the foot as the body's weight is transferred from the heel to the big toe. This inward turn is generally accompanied by an inward rotation of the shin bone (tibial axial rotation).[8] The combination of excessive pronation with the inward twisting of the tibia can be responsible for a number of foot, shin and knee problems that are often associated with running. These problems can often be reduced by the use of the proper orthotics. Medical doctors, podiatrists and chiropractors can fit them for you. There are also some orthotics that can be purchased from sporting goods stores. They are made for traditional problems in feet and might or might not work for you.

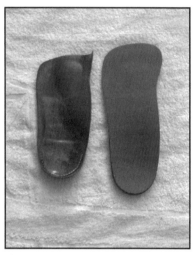

Orthonics

Heel cups can reduce or prevent some problems. The hard plastic heel cups can make up for poor-fitting heels in your shoes. The soft rubber cups absorb shocks and help to prevent or ease those problems that are caused by continued stress. Heel spurs, plantar fasciitis and shin splints are some of the problems that can be aided with rubber heel cups.

Ankle braces have been helpful to some runners in preventing overpronation. While the primary use for most braces is to prevent sprains to the outer part of the ankle, they also reduce inward rotation. There are two types of ankle braces: those that encase the ankle and limit much of the movement: and those that limit the inward and outward tilting around the foot's long axis but still allow the ankle to freely flex

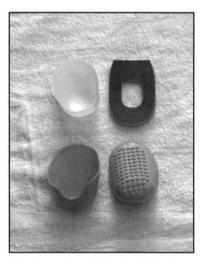

Heel cups: top left, plastic heel cup for support; top right, heel pad with cutout to protect stone bruises; bottom, soft rubber heel cup (top and bottom view) for cushioning.

and extend. The latter type is the one that walkers and runners would want.

REDUCING SHOE-RELATED FOOT PROBLEMS

Break in the shoes slowly. New shoes might take a while to adjust to your feet. Blisters are more likely to occur with new shoes, so take care.

The left shoe is laced correctly – top down through each eyelet. The right shoe is incorrectly laced.

Wearing two pairs of thin socks helps reduce the chances of developing a blister.

The proper way to lace a pair of shoes would be to put the laces into each eyelet from the top down rather than from the bottom up. The only exception is at the top eyelet where the lace is threaded from the bottom up because it is easier to tie. If laces go over the top of the eyelet, the laces help hold the shoe snug; the laces won't loosen halfway through the contest or workout. When you put on your shoes, tighten them at the bottom eyelets, then tighten them at each succeeding eyelet up to the top eyelet where you tie the shoes. Doing these things will hold your foot in the proper position, preventing it from sliding forward and causing black toenail or blisters.

SPIKED SHOES

If you are competing in events held on a track, particularly the sprints, you might want to wear spikes. The spiked shoes should be snug fitting and light. Always carry an extra pair of laces, extra spikes and a spike *key* in your bag. It is useful to have a pair of spikes relevant for the demands of the training units and a special pair of competition spikes. The shoes should always be cleaned, dried and aired after training. Laces and spikes should also be checked after workouts and races.

CLOTHING AND SOCKS

Socks are much more important than most people realize. Synthetic fibers that whisk away perspiration are best. Most people reduce the chances of blisters if they wear two pair of thin socks rather than one pair of thick socks. Your socks should fit snugly and should not have seams that might create a blister.

Your clothing should fit the weather. If it is warm, shorts are best. The more skin that is exposed to the air, the more quickly body heat is transferred to the air as the perspiration evaporates. Be sure that the seams in the shorts do not irritate your legs when you run. Running shorts with built-in briefs are generally most comfortable. Shirt materials that *breathe* are also important. Cotton absorbs perspiration and lets it sit on your body. This allows for more cooling of your body through the evaporation of the perspiration. If you are wearing a T-shirt that is wet, you will get more cooling if you leave it on rather than changing to a dry shirt. (More on cooling in Chapter 12.)

If you are exercising in cooler or cold air, you will want warmer clothes that will wick away your perspiration. Wool underwear is effective. Many high-tech materials such as polypropylene and Thermax are also quite effective. Cotton is not. By wearing several thinner layers you can take off layers as you warm up. Over your underwear, you might need a wool or synthetic turtleneck or sweater. For your outside layer, a material that *breathes*, such as Gore-tex, allows body heat and perspiration to escape.

Be sure to keep your head warm if the air is cold. A cap prevents the head from getting chilled. Much of your body heat is lost through your head. When it is very cold, gloves or mittens should be worn. An absorbent or lined sweat suit or training suit is a good idea for cold-weather running, although some people prefer the sleeker-looking lycra tights.

Many women wear jogging bras. Some women insist on them, while others prefer not wearing a bra. The objective of the bra is support. If you are large-breasted, it is very important. Berlei and Bendon make excellent support bras. You want a bra that does not chafe. Stretch lycra and cross-strapped bras are generally best.

OTHER CONCERNS

Skin protection is very important when exercising in the sun. Exposure to the sun not only ages the skin but also increases the chances for skin cancer, particularly for those with light complexions. Sun protection for the skin and lips is available at every pharmacy and should be used appropriately. For most people, an SPF factor of 15 or higher is recommended.

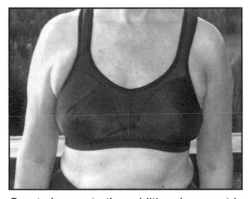 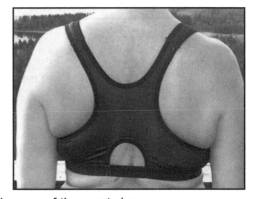

Sports bra: note the additional support in the rear of the sports bra.

Wearing a cap in summer is also wise. Your summer cap might be wide-brimmed to keep the sun off of the back of your neck. If you are more concerned with shading your eyes, a baseball-style cap with a visor will work.

Other accessories you might consider are:

A *pulse monitor* that works by strapping a belt around the chest. The belt picks up your heart rate, then transfers it to a wrist-watch-type monitor that provides a continual readout of your heart rate. Most also have timers. Some of these also have stopwatch capabilities. They are usually available at sporting goods or fitness stores at a cost of $70 and up.

Sunglasses are a must for many people. They not only protect the eyes, but they reduce the need to squint through the sunlight. Green or gray are the most effective colors for the lenses.

If you have a tendency toward developing blisters or other chafing, you might carry some *petroleum jelly* or other skin lubricant with you. Sometimes the shorts or underwear irritate the thigh skin, so a coat of Vasoline might reduce the chafing.

It is best not to wear earphones because you cannot hear street noises, such as cars and ambulances or other humans and animals. Better to hear the barking dog before you feel its bite! If you insist on listening to tunes, keep the volume low and listen with only one earphone so that one ear can hear the outside world. You must be continually aware.

If you are going to run at night, wear reflective material or carry a light. Reflective vests, shoes and arm straps are available that will make you visible in the headlights of approaching traffic.

Handheld weights are not a recommended accessory. They merely add to the load that your feet and legs must support, and they aren't very beneficial for your arms. If you want to increase arm strength, see the conditioning chapter for effective exercises.

Your *training bag* should always carry an icepack, a towel, basic toilet requisites, some talcum powder, petroleum jelly, a sun block, a hat or cap, extra socks and some safety pins.

Notes

1. Marshall, R.N., D.B. Myers and D.G. Palmer. "Disturbance of gait due to Rheumatoid Disease" *Journal of Rheumatology* 7:5 (1980): 617-623.
2. Henning, E.M. "Biomechanical variables and perception of cushioning for running in various types of footwear." *Journal of Applied Biomechanics* 12:1 (1996): 143-150.
3. Aerts, P. and D. DeClerq. "Deformation characteristics of the heel region of the shod foot during a simulated heel strike: the effect

of varying midsole hardness." *Journal of Sports Sciences* 11:5 (1993): 449-461.

4. Reinchmidt, C. and B.M.Nigg. "Influence of heel height on ankle joint moments in running." *Medicine and Science in Sports and Exercise.* 27:3 (1995): 410-416.

5. Christopher, J. et al, in P. Cavanagh. *Biomechanics of Distance Running.* Champaign, IL: Human Kinetics,1990, 156-157.

6. Stacoff, A. et al. "The effects of shoes on the torsion and rearfoot motion in running." *Medicine and Science in Sports and Exercise.* 23:4 (1991): 482-490.

7. Stacoff, A. et al. "The torsion of the foot in running." *International Journal of Sport Biomechanics.* 5:4 (1989): 375-389.

8. Nawoczenski, D.A. et al. "The effect of foot orthotics on three-dimensional kinematics of the leg and rearfoot during running." *Journal of Orthopedic and Sports Physical Therapy.*" 21:6 (1995): 317-327.

3

TIGHTNESS AND LOOSENESS

Different types of exercise require varying amounts of *flexibility* in the joints and varying amounts of *stiffness* of the muscle fibers. (Muscle stiffness relates to the tension in the individual muscle fibers. It will be discussed later in the chapter.) Walking and distance running are more efficient if muscles are stiffer and a person's range of motion (flexibility) is not excessive. Gymnastics or dance, on the other hand, require great flexibility in the joints as well as muscle stiffness. Most of us have been given the impression that being flexible is always good and that stretching before a practice or a competition is a sacred duty. Recent research indicates that this might not always be true.

In this chapter, we will look at why stretching in sport is being re-evaluated. The fact that many north European track and field coaches have stopped stretching their sprinters gives us pause to think that perhaps the traditions with which we have been raised, both in physical education classes and athletic teams, might be in error.

We will begin our exploration of the body's movement potentials by looking at the bones, joints and connective tissues. Flexibility is sought primarily to increase range of motion by stretching the connective tissue around the joint; however, it might also be stretching connective tissue around the muscle and also stretching the muscle. Then, we will look at the effect on the muscle fibers. (This chapter gets a bit technical, but it is neccessary if you want to understand your musculature.)

THE FUNCTIONS OF CONNECTIVE TISSUES IN THE BODY

When we stretch, we are affecting the skeletal system, the muscular system or both. Connective tissues are essential elements in both systems. The body's connective tissues are composed largely of a protein called *collagen*. It is the most common type of protein in the body. Collagen has two very important factors: it is very strong and it is highly resistant to stretching. One study showed that a force 10,000 times greater than the weight of a fiber of collagen would not change its length.[1]

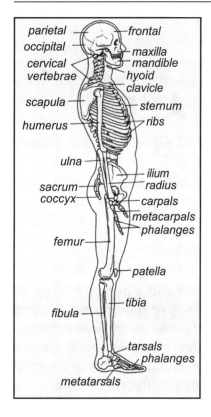

parietal — frontal
occipital —
cervical — maxilla
vertebrae — mandible
hyoid
clavicle
scapula — sternum
humerus — ribs
ulna —
ilium
sacrum — radius
coccyx —
carpals
metacarpals
phalanges
femur —
patella
tibia
fibula —
tarsals
phalanges
metatarsals

There are five major types of collagen. The most common (type I) is found in both ligaments and tendons as well as in skin and bone. But there are also elastic-like tissues in our ligaments and tendons — more in the ligaments. Consequently, we have cells in our connective tissues that stretch quite well and other cells that resist stretching. It is the latter which is our concern in developing adequate flexibility.

The skeletal system is made up of more than 200 bones, each connected to adjacent bones by connective tissue called *ligaments.* Nearly all bones are attached to other bones by ligaments. Each joining of bones is a *joint.* Some joints, such as the wrist or shoulder, are very mobile, which allows many types of motion. Other joints are immobile or nearly immobile. Examples would be the joints of the ribs with the sternum (breastbone) or the joints of the fibula and tibia in the lower leg.

There are a number of types of joints in the body. Some joints, such as the knee, merely serve as hinges. Some, like the hip and shoulder, are ball-and-socket joints. Others, such as the wrist and ankle, slide one bone on another. Others allow for rotation or other types of movement.

It is in these joints that your range of motion is determined. If your elbow joint is too loose or if there is an unusual shape at the end of the bones, the arm might be able to be bent backward past the normal straight position. Called a *hyperextension*, this is caused by an unusual laxity in the elbow joint. If you have normally tight ligaments in the hip joint, which connects to the thigh bone (femur), but you wanted to be a ballet dancer able to lift your leg forward to a 120-degree or greater angle, you would need to stretch the ligaments in the back of the joint capsule to allow for such a movement. The same would be true if you wanted to be able to do the splits for dancing, cheerleading, gymnastics or kicking a soccer ball. You would need stretched ligaments in both the front and the rear of your hip joint.

The average person will not want to stretch the ligaments much because it can weaken the basic structure of the joints. However, as opposed to tendons, ligaments are slightly more elastic so as to allow greater movement of the joints. Some ligaments, especially some found in the neck and lower back, are quite elastic.

Runners who want to increase the range of motion of a specific joint might desire to stretch their ligaments. And there are occasional abnormalities of the joints that require some stretching in order to allow for a full range of motion. These situations should be left to medical specialists for diagnosis.

But increases in flexibility do not always aid an athlete's performance. In one of the earliest studies in the area, Herb DeVries found that great increases in flexibility did not improve running time in the 100-yard dash.[2] Also, tighter subjects are more efficient in walking than the looser subjects.[3]

The muscular system contains a number of types of connective tissues. There are the *tendons* (which connect muscle to bone) and the collagen sheaths, which encircle both the large muscles and the small muscle fibers within those muscles.

It is the function of the tendons to be able to transmit all of the force generated by the muscle to the bone onto which it connects. Obviously if the tendon stretched, it would not be able to transmit the force effectively. It would be like trying to tow a car with a rubber band rather than with a chain. If a tendon is stretched more than four percent, it is likely to be injured.

In stretching exercises, we are primarily concerned with stretching the collagen fibers in the muscular system. A lack of flexibility commonly appears when the connective tissues in the muscles or the tendons shorten. This begins to happen as we grow older or become inactive. In the old days of weight lifting and body building, it was a common occurrence. We called it being "muscle bound." Now, we know that it was not the muscles that were bound but that the inflexibility came from a failure to stretch the connective tissue. The problem with the old-time body builders was that they did not do their exercises through a full range of motion. Consequently, the connective tissue in their biceps muscles was short from biceps curls in which they did not fully extend their arms and did not allow them to completely straighten their arms. Also, the connective tissues in their chests were shortened from bench presses that did not allow the bar to drop to the chest.

Fascia is a term applied to connective tissue that is not otherwise identifiable as ligaments, tendons or other common types of collagen. A few examples:

- Fascia that binds the muscle fibers and encases the muscle belly.
- Fascia that binds our organs and holds them in place.
- Fascia under the skin.

As we contract a muscle when moving something, some of the muscle's power is used to overcome internal friction and tension. The fascia between the muscle fibers and around them are said to provide more then 40 percent of that internal resistance that the muscle encounters in developing its force. The joint capsule (because of the friction of one bone moving against another plus the tightness of the connective tissue in and around the joint) provides about 47 percent of the internal resistance. The muscle's tendon accounts for about 10 percent of the internal resistance and the skin adds another two percent to the total resistance.

With these resistance factors in mind, stretching the connective tissues in the areas in which you need extra efficiency should be of value, especially if you are interested in efficiency of movement because you are a dancer or a competitive athlete. Such stretching not only increases your range of motion but can also reduce your chances of injury when exerting yourself in a way that overly stretches the connective tissue.

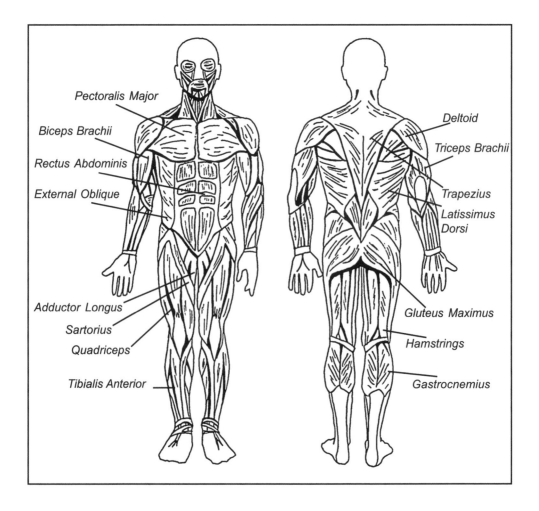

RANGE OF MOTION

In each of the above types of movement, your joints will exhibit greater or lesser amounts of movement ability. Your range of motion is the measure of flexibility for each joint or combination of joints. That range of motion is determined by both the connective tissues (ligaments) that surround the joint and by the tendons and the tension in the muscle fibers. When the muscle tension is very high, the muscle is said to be in a state of *contracture*. The contractures can generally be reduced within a few weeks by effective stretching exercises. Movement restriction caused by tight ligaments generally takes much longer.

Some people are very concerned with increasing their range of motion. Most dancers need great flexibility. Many athletes also need additional flexibility that is beyond what is normally needed for day-to-day living. Hurdlers, divers, high jumpers, soccer kickers, swimmers and gymnasts are just a few of those who might need to increase their range of motion in order to be more effective in their chosen activities.

THE EFFECTS OF AGING ON CONNECTIVE TISSUES

Sixty to 70 percent of our connective tissues are water when we are young. As we age, our connective tissues become more brittle. By age 70 we have lost about 20 percent of the water content that was in our connective tissues when we were born. So, our total water has been reduced to approximately 50 percent of the connective tissues. In addition, our collagen becomes thicker, so we become stiffer and less flexible. Also, the collagen in our skin loses its ability to spring back, causing us to get wrinkles.

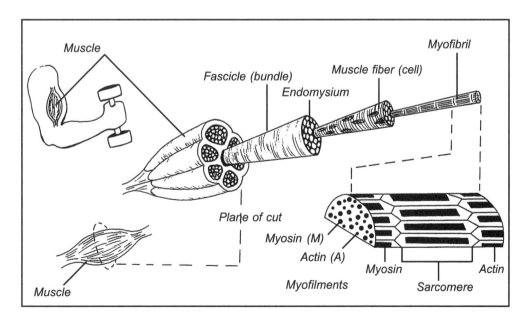

We can reduce the aging of our connective tissues if we maintain an effective stretching program throughout our lives. But even those who have not maintained a routine to retain flexibility can undo much of the damage of inactivity by beginning to stretch correctly.

What does stretching do? Recent research is making us question our previously unquestioned reliance on stretching for warming up and as an aid to reducing *delayed onset muscle soreness* (DOMS) and as way to reduce injuries. While we have always known that stretching was good and more stretching was better, there are now a number of questions.

Among them: Is stretching as a warmup good for some people and not good for others? Is it good for the treatment of some injuries but not for others?

Certainly, when you need a greater range of motion (ROM), stretching is essential. The question is how much range of motion do you need? If you are a cyclist, you might not need much. If you swim the backstroke, you might not need much additional shoulder flexibility but a butterfly swimmer might need additional shoulder flexibility in order to be able to allow the arms to clear the water during the recovery. Yet, both might need extra flexibility for their sprint turns.

If you are a jogger or marathon runner, you probably don't need extra hip flexibility, but if you are a sprinter you might need more. So the speed at which you run might be a factor in determining whether you need extra flexibility. The faster you run, the longer your stride, so the greater the amount of hip flexion or extension you might need.

Stretching during a warmup increases injuries for at least some people. A couple of studies of 10K runners found that those who stretched had more injuries than those who did not. The question is: Was it the stretching itself or just poor stretching technique that was the culprit?

Relative to injury, one study found that when one joint had at least a 15 percent greater flexibility than the corresponding joint, the more flexible joint was 2.6 times more likely to be injured.[4] A hypothesis for this might be that the stretching exercises lengthened the connective tissue that surrounds the muscle fibers, which then required the muscle fibers to absorb all of the force of the eccentric contractions (the muscle lengthening while it is being contracted, such as when you land on your toes when running — the calf muscle lengthens while it is resisting the force of the landing). The theory is that too much force was placed on the fibers. They overstretched and were injured.

A study in New Zealand measured the effect on the dorsiflexion of the ankle (toes moving upward) and compared stretching (five 30-second ankle stretches); running (10 minutes on a treadmill at 60 percent of the maximum heart rate for the subject's age); and a combination of the two: first running, then stretching. The results showed that muscle stiffness was more effectively reduced by jogging, but the range of motion was more effectively increased by either the stretching or a combination of running followed by stretching.[5] A study at the University of Queensland in Australia showed that warmup and stretching did not decrease muscle stiffness, but intense exercise did.[6]

Stretching might decrease injuries, at least for some people

In an American study of military recruits, the group that added three hamstring stretching exercises to its physical fitness regime increased both its hamstring flexibility and reduced the rate of overuse injuries to the legs from 29.1 percent in the control group to 16.7 percent in the group that stretched.[7]

Some questions about the recent research

How we measure flexibility affects what we find. Currently, we have no way of knowing just how much we are stretching the muscle fibers and how much we are stretching the various connective tissues involved. When the research relates to injuries, the studies have not reported whether the injuries were to the muscle fibers, the tendons or the ligaments. They also don't report on whether the injury was acute (an injury from a single specific movement) or a chronic overuse injury due to repeating the same movement patterns thousands of times, perhaps on a surface that aids in the injury — such as running on concrete versus running on grass or in the sand.

Muscular injuries due to reduced muscle stiffness

Are muscular injuries such as strains or pulls increased or decreased by stretching? Does stretching before the exercise increase the susceptibility of the muscle fibers to injury during the activity when the muscle's job is to shorten?

The muscles are stretched more than the connective tissue. This can set the muscle up for more injury and reduce the muscle stiffness by relaxing the muscles.[8 9 10]

To understand a bit better, we must remember that while tendons might be stretched to four percent before injury and muscles can usually be stretched to 20 percent or 30 percent before they are injured, each of u us — and each muscle and tendon — differ somewhat. Therefore, we don't know exactly how far any of our own muscle groups can be stretched before an injury either occurs or becomes more probable with our ensuing exercise.

Naturally, much of the work on stretching muscles or tendons to the breaking point has to be done with animals or excised muscles from dead animals. Do these studies hold true for human tissue? If a rabbit's front leg muscle fibers can withstand a 20 percent stretch without ill effect, does that mean that a human leg muscle fiber can only withstand 20 percent? What about a human neck muscle? What about another rabbit's leg or neck? What about your leg muscle fibers compared to those of your sister, your neighbor or the Olympic sprint champion? Lots of questions! But realistically, studying the muscle fibers of a rabbit's leg or a bird's wing will give us some indication as to how muscles react. And at this stage of the game, all we are seeing are indications — but indications that are strong enough that we should take them into account in training.

At the Duke University Medical Center, an interesting study was performed with leg muscles in the front of the lower leg of rabbits. It was found that when the muscles were stretched by 20 percent, they didn't seem to have their potential contracting force reduced. But muscles stretched 30 percent were not able to exert maximum force. Additionally, the fibers near the tendons at the end of the muscle belly showed ruptures and bleeding. Certainly, the 30 percent stretch injured some fibers. Is this what causes more injuries in 10K runners who stretch? The study also concluded that when the fibers lost their ability to contract to the fullest, they also increased their chance for injury.[11]

The stretch of the muscle can make it less able to contract (shorten) efficiently. Therefore, this reduces its stiffness. A study at the Centinella Hospital Biomechanics Laboratory, a major Southern California sports medicine center, might indicate why. The study found that electrical activity in muscles was generally reduced by stretching, whether the stretching was before or after a warmup. This was particularly true for the calf muscles (soleus and gastrocnemius) after a warmup.[12]

Muscle stiffness

Muscle stiffness might be mechanical, due to the properties in the muscle fibers, or neural, due to increased electrical activity in the nerves, which then stimulate the muscle fibers and make them more tense. While the aforementioned contractures are excessive stiffness and will reduce one's performance, a certain amount of stiffness is valuable for most athletic movements because power is increased with the right amount of stiffness.

Mechanical properties of muscles

Extensibility or stiffness of muscle fibers is related to how easily or difficult it is to lengthen the muscle fibers when a lengthening force is applied to them.[13] We measure the stiffness of a muscle by seeing how much it lengthens when it is affected by a force that should stretch it.

Muscles that lengthen rather easily are called *compliant*. Those that don't stretch readily are called stiff. More technically, stiffness is defined as the ratio of change in force to the change in the length of the muscle. This stiffness is dependant to a large degree on the tension within the muscle fibers. That tension can come from the activation by the nerves or from factors within the muscle.

The myosin and actin proteins, which move across each other when the muscle fiber contracts — thereby shortening the muscle fiber — are attached by what is termed a *myosin cross bridge*. The strength of that attachment by the cross bridge is what sustains a muscular contraction and what causes the stiffness of a muscle. The stronger the tension of the cross bridge, the more the muscle resists stretching. So, the more it is considered to be stiff. (More on this in the next chapter.)

Some of those factors can be hereditary. Environmental factors might also be present. For example, when a stretch-shortening (plyometric) stress occurs, such as when you jump down from a chair and immediately jump upward, there is much greater tension developed in the muscle fibers than if you are merely standing on the chair. The tension required in the muscles to absorb the force of jumping from 18 inches above the floor is significant.

Stretching a muscle (as during eccentric or lengthening action) increases the firing rate of the muscle spindles, which increases the stiffness of the muscle. (The spindles sense the amount of stretch in muscle fibers and signal the information to the spinal column.) Therefore, the stiffness of the muscle will also be influenced by the level of muscle activation.

Continued activity, such as running, in which the muscle lengthens under pressure (eccentric contraction), then immediately contracts (called the stretch-shortening cycle), obviously causes fatigue in the muscles. Part of that fatigue is due to normal fatiguing factors such as increased waste products from the energy generating system, but fatigue also results from reduced muscle stiffness when the exercise requires more energy to contract the muscles.[14] So, muscle stiffness also slows the fatigue factor, especially in strength-speed activities like running 100 to 400 meters.

Notes

1. Verzar, F. "Aging of Collagen." *Scientific American* 208:4 (1963): 104-117.
2. DeVries, H.A. The "looseness" factor in speed and O2 consumption in an anaerobic 100-yard dash." *Research Quarterly for Exercise*

and Sport 34 (1963): 305-313.

3. Gleim, GW, N.S. Stachenfield, J.A. Nicholas. "The influence of flexibility on the economy of walking and jogging." *Journal of Orthopedic Research* 8 (1990):814-823.

4. Knapic, J.J., C. Bauman, B.H. Jones, J.M. Harris, L. Vaughan. "Preseason strength and flexibility imbalances associated with athletic injuries in female collegiate athletes," *American Journal of Sports Medicine* 19 (1991): 76-81.

5. McNair, P.J., S.N. Stanley. "Effect of passive stretching and jogging on the series elastic muscle stiffness and range of motion of the ankle joint." *British Journal of Sports Medicine* 30:4 (1996): 313-318.

6. Smeathers, J.E. "Muscle stiffness" Presentation at the Pre-Olympic Scientific Congress. Brisbane, Australia. Sept. 12, 2000.

7. Hartig, D.E., J.M. Henderson. "Increasing hamstring flexibility decreases lower extremity overuse injuries in military basic trainees." *American Journal of Sports Medicine* 27:2 (1999):173-6.

8. Schultz, P. "Flexibility: Day of the stretch," *Physician and Sportsmedecine* 7 (1979): 109-117.

9. Taylor, D.C., J.D. Dalton, A.V. Seaber, W.E. Garrett. "Viscoelastic properties of muscle-tendon units: The biomechanical effects of stretching." *American Journal of Sports Medicine* 18 (1990): 300-309.

10. Taylor, DC, A.V. Seaber, W.E. Garrett, "Response of muscle tendon units to cyclic repetitive stretching." *Trans Orthrop Res Soc* 10 (1985): 84.

11. Noonan, T.J., T.M. Best, A.V. Seaber, W.E. Garrett, Jr. "Identification of a threshold for skeletal muscle injury." *American Journal of Sports Medicine* 22:2 (1994): 257-61.

12. Mohr, K.J., M.M. Pink, C. Elsner, R.S. Kvitne. "Electromyographic investigation of stretching: the effect of warm-up." *Clinical Journal of Sport Medicine* 8:3 (1998): 215-20.

13. Taylor, D.O., J.D. Dalton, A.V. Seaber, W.E. Garrett. "Viscoelastic Properties of Muscle-Tendon Units." *American Journal of Sports Medicine.* 18:3 (1990): 300-308.

14. Avela, J., P.V. Komi. "Interaction between muscle stiffness and stretch reflex sensitivity after long-term stretch-shortening cycle exercise." *Muscle Nerve* 21:9 (1998): 1224-1227.

4

WARMING UP EFFECTIVELY

Most of us have learned that we must warm up and stretch before participating in an activity. The research indicates that stretching, especially for runners, can predispose us to injury, particularly muscle and tendon injuries.

The part of the traditional warm up that is now questionable is the pre-exercise stretch. While it has been common practice to stretch prior to physical activity, recent research indicates that stretching before the workout is not always recommended. It might increase the risk of injury and reduce your potential strength.[1] The traditional reasons for stretching (getting the muscles ready to contract, reducing injury possibility, reducing the muscle soreness that might develop, etc.) all now seem to be at least questionable, if not downright wrong.

The reasons we have been given for stretching include:

1. Warming up the muscles and making them more ready to contract.

2. Reducing the amount of delayed onset muscle soreness (DOMS), which is common, particularly in untrained or poorly trained exercisers. This is a major reason for people stretching after a workout.

3. Reducing the chance for muscle injuries.

The research, although inconclusive due to the relatively few studies done so far, indicates that all three of these reasons are probably wrong for most people who exercise.

A number of studies indicate that the muscles function less well after stretching because the stiffness required for maximal force is reduced by the stretching. Delayed onset muscle soreness does not seem to be reduced by stretching or massage. Muscle and connective tissue injuries are generally higher among those who stretch.

A meta-analysis (analysis of all or most of the known studies in the area) has shown that stretching alone generally does not prevent injuries. It either did not prevent injuries or it increased injuries. In further summarizing literature of basic physiology and anatomy, it was found that:

1. Stretching doesn't increase the compliance (effective action) of a muscle during eccentric (lengthening) contractions. These lengthening contractions are the type of contractions most often associated with muscle and tendon injury. The calf muscles (gastrocnemius and soleus) are in lengthening contractions when you land on your toes while running.

2. Stretching can produce damage at the cellular level of muscles and tendons.

3. Stretching seems to mask muscular pain in humans. This anesthetic effect seems to be why stretching an injured muscle or tendon might make it feel better even though additional damage may be occurring.

4. Stretching before an exercise will have no positive effect on a muscle that will not be required to elongate during the activity, such as jogging or walking. Yet, studies of joggers and slow running indicate that stretching can cause injuries.[2]

An Australian study of military recruits during 12 weeks of training, in which half did stretching exercises and half did not, found that "a typical muscle-stretching protocol performed during pre-exercise warm ups does not produce clinically meaningful reductions in risk of exercise-related injury in army recruits. Fitness may be an important, modifiable risk factor."[3]

Should stretching be part of your warm up?

One thing we know is that we are all individuals with our own potentials or problems relative to our muscles and connective tissues. Some people like to stretch as part of their warm up and some do not. You might need to experiment on stretching versus nonstretching in your warm up. If you stretch, you might want to experiment with the types of stretches you do and whether or not you should stretch to the maximum degree possible.

As indicated earlier, research on stretching has not answered all, or even most, of our questions on whether to stretch or how to stretch. Is stretching a poor warm up for a distance runner but a necessary factor for a high jumper or dancer? We don't know. Distance runners are currently studied more often than other athletes in terms of the desirability of stretching. So far, the results indicate that for long-distance running, stretching is not effective as an injury preventive for most people.

A 1983 survey of 500 runners found that those who warmed up had more injuries than those who did not (87.7 percent vs. 66 percent), and the frequency of injuries increased with the length of the warm up. It is assumed that stretching was part of the warm up but it was not specifically asked.[4] A few years later, a survey of 10K runners in the national championships found that those who stretched had more injuries. But it is not known whether those who stretched did so because they already had an injury and assumed that the stretching would protect them from further injury.[5]

In a yearlong study of recreational distance runners, it was found that those who sometimes stretched had more injuries than those who always stretched or those who never stretched. But those who never stretched had fewer new injuries than those who stretched.[6] While the above studies cast doubt as to the effectiveness of stretching for distance runners, more and better research needs to be done.

Some people stretch because they believe that it will reduce the soreness that can follow exercise. A Swedish study investigated whether stretching would decrease DOMS in women doing eccentric exercise, the type of exercise most likely to increase muscle soreness. No advantages for stretching were found. The amount of soreness and tenderness was not reduced.[7]

A number of other studies indicate that stretching does not seem to reduce the effects of DOMS either. This is the residual pain often found in untrained people who begin exercise programs. It can last up to a week.[8] [9] [10]

Increasing one's range of motion by stretching prior to exercise also does not seem to work.[11]

In some activities, you can stretch too long or too far during your warm up. If you are entering a sprint race, you would want your muscle fibers to be tighter and stiffer. Too much stretch can slow you down. This is also true of jumpers — high jumpers or long jumpers, swimmers and weightlifters. But if you are getting ready for a tennis match, a long run or a leisurely afternoon of skiing, light stretching might not be a problem.[12] More research is now being conducted into the effectiveness of warm up stretching for various types of activities.

A number of studies have shown that stretching reduces speed and power by four to eight percent. One of the most recent was done in Australia.[13] It found an increase in the maximum power output for people who did not stretch. The study involved four groups of subjects. Each group did five minutes of jogging first. Then, one group did the traditional "static" stretching (calf muscles, gluteals and quadriceps — front of thigh), where the person stretches slowly to the maximum extent. The second group did proprioceptive neuromuscular facilitated stretching (PNF) in which an assistant helps the participant to stretch while the participant stretches one muscle while forcibly contracting the opposite muscle. (If the participant is stretching the hamstrings in the rear of the thigh, she contracts the quadriceps in the front of the thigh while the assistant helps to increase the stretch.) The third group contracted each of the three muscle groups forcefully but did not stretch. The fourth, or control, group only jogged.

The test was to see how high a person could jump from a resting position, then how high she could jump in a drop jump — which would be more similar to running. (In a drop jump, the person jumps down from a box, then immediately rebounds as high as possible. This is more similar to running where you land on your foot, absorb the shock and immediately push off the ground.) The results showed that the control group did the best, the group that contracted the muscles — but did not stretch — was second, the PNF group (which involved stretching and muscular contraction) was third best and the typical static stretching was worst. For the resting jump, called a "squat jump," there was a two percent increase in power for those who did not stretch. For the box jump, there was a seven percent increase in power for those who did not stretch.

With this newer research in mind, we can say that stretching before a workout or competition might be a problem. "The evidence suggests that athletes should drop the stretching before exercise and increase the warm up."[14] On the other hand, if you stretch after your workout — when the connective tissues are warmer — you should be able to increase your flexibility effectively as long as the stretching is not so hard that you set yourself up for an injury on your next training day.

Warming up the muscles to make them more efficient

There doesn't seem to be any disagreement about using sport-specific movements in the warm up. Running or walking seem to be effective in getting the blood supply opened to the muscles that will be used in your workout or competition. If your workout is walking fast, warm up by walking at a normal pace, then increasing your speed. If you are merely going to jog, slow jogging for a minute should be enough. But if you are going to sprint or even run a mile or two at a good pace, warm up the muscles with slow then faster speeds until you have done some running at the pace you will use in your workout or competition. There is basic scientific evidence to suggest that active warm up might be protective against muscle strain injury.

A German study on the calf muscles measuring muscle reflexes and force development after stretching, running 10 minutes or with no prior warm up indicated that the force development was about the same for the running warm up and no warm up and was considerably less (about five percent) after stretching. There was, however, a great deal of difference among the 50 subjects in how each reacted to the various types of warm ups.[15] This might indicate that some people need to be stretched in their warm up, while most people do not. A Japanese study using only five women as a part of a larger study found that the warm up reduced the amount of muscle damage due to eccentric contractions.[16]

If the purpose of stretching is to get the muscle ready to contract more quickly, this doesn't seem to happen. While we often said in the past that a stretched muscle is more ready to contract, as shown in the knee-jerk reflex, this does not seem to be true. An electromyographic study of the firing patterns (electrical stimulation of the muscle from the nervous system) of the bicep femoris, soleus and gastrocnemius indicates that the stretching reduces the firing patterns in these muscles.[17]

A study at the University of Pennsylvania indicates that, at least with sprinters, even a slight physical warm up can increase the ability of the muscles to pick up oxygen through increased mitochondrial activity (activity in the cells or the muscle). So, even a somewhat relaxed movement pattern can help the muscles to bridge the gap from anaerobic to aerobic energy production.[18]

Warm up and anaerobic capacity increase

An Australian study that might have limited application to most situations because it involved full-speed cycling for one minute on a bicycle ergometer in 86-degree heat is nevertheless interesting. One warm up consisted of four 30-second maximum sprints (100 percent VO_2 max), while the other warm up consisted of applying hot packs to the quadriceps muscles for an hour. The differences between the groups were only found during the first 30 seconds of the test. Those who had actively warmed up had greater potential to use oxygen during that first 30 seconds.[19]

While admitting that "there is little scientific support for the benefits of warm up," athletes commonly warm up prior to activity with the intention of improving performance and reducing the incidence of injuries. A Canadian study compared a group not warming up with groups warming up at 60, 70 and 80 percent of their VO_2 max. The warm up

---

VO_2 means the maximum (max) volume (V) of oxygen (O_2) which can be consumed in milliliters per minute. It is generally considered to be the best indication of aerobic fitness. Major marathon winners are generally in the high 60s or low 70s. An Italian cyclist had a 95 and the best yet recorded is a Norwegian cross-country skier, with a 96 VO_2 max.

groups followed their aerobic warm up with leg stretches. It was found that while ankle and hip extension ranges of movement were increased under all warm up protocols, hip flexion (bringing the thigh forward) increased only when the exercise warm up was at 80 percent of maximum. The maximum anaerobic potentials were realized after the 70 percent VO$_2$ max warm up. The study recommended a 15-minute warm up at 60 to 70 percent of the VO$_2$ max.[20]

Warm up and the positive effect on the heart

At New York University, a study of heart function, using nuclear imaging after strenuous exercise — both with and without a warm up — found no difference in the work of the heart with or without a warm up. These findings are contradictory to other such studies.[21]

Warm up and increased endurance

A French study used untrained young men exercising to exhaustion on a bicycle exerciser at 75 percent of maximum heart rate. One trial was without a warm up and one was with a 15-minute warm up (50 percent of maximum heart rate). The warm up was found to allow better adjustment of the heat-regulating mechanisms of the body and the blood flow. It also increased the water loss during physical work. For most subjects, these adjustments allowed for improved endurance during the exercise.[22]

Warming up the breathing muscles

Just as other muscles need conditioning and can profit by a warm up, so can the breathing muscles (diaphragm, intercostals, abdominals, sternocleidomastoid and others). When the diaphragm contracts, it lowers the bottom of the thorax and enlarges the available space in the thorax, which reduces the pressure and creates a vacuum. The outside air then moves in. The external intercostals (muscles between the ribs and near the skin) also expand the rib cage, which also increases the space inside the thorax. When these muscles relax, the area inside the thorax is reduced and the air is forced out.

During exercise, additional breathing muscles can come into play. The sternocleidomastoid can lift the top of the front of the rib cage, enlarging it even more. The trapezius can do the same with the back ribs. Also during exercise, additional muscles help to force the air out. The abdominal muscles can help to push the diaphragm even higher and the internal intercostal muscles pull the ribs closer together. Both of these reduce the thorax volume even more, so the internal pressure is increased and the air is exhaled even more forcefully.

A study at England's Birmingham University looked at warming up the breathing muscles. An untrained group and a group of elite rowers did breathing tests and warm up exercises. The recommendation after the test was that specific breathing warm ups be done along with the full body warm ups.[23]

Recommended warm up

Based on the results, of the research it would seem that most people should not stretch. In fact, probably no one should stretch because the stretching reduces the muscles' stiffness and their ability to contract to the maximum. It also seems to set them up for more chance of injury during eccentric contractions that occur in most running and jumping exercises. The exception would be for those with overly tight muscles (contractures) whose efficiency will be increased by reducing the excessive tightness.

The research tells us that for a maximum effort, such as a hard competition, about 15 minutes of exercise at about 60 to 70 percent of the athlete's VO_2 max should be effective. The VO_2 max (maximum volume of oxygen) is the major physiological measurement used by exercise physiologists. It determines the amount of oxygen that a body can use to develop energy while exercising. (The maximum amount of oxygen used [VO_2 max] is the number of milliliters [ml] of oxygen [O_2] per kilogram of body weight per minute.)

The American College of Sports Medicine (ASCM) has recommended that we can find our approximate VO_2 max by taking 220 heartbeats per minute, then subtracting our age. This would give you your maximum heart rate for your age. You would then decide to work out at between 55 and 90 percent of that maximum heart rate. The left column on the following shows varying percentages of that maximum heart rate at which you might work out or warm up. The middle column shows the ACSM's approximation of the VO_2 max at which you are probably exercising. Sport scientists at Marshall University did their own study seeking to validate the ASCM's VO_2 max calculations. They found that you would have to work at a slightly higher heart rate to achieve the VO_2 max that the ASCM had proposed. So, to achieve a 40 VO_2 max, the ASCM says that you need to exercise at only 55 percent of your maximum heart rate. Marshall calculates that to be 63 percent of your maximum heart rate.

By using the Marshall University study and the ASCM guidelines, we can approximate the amount of aerobic warm up level needed in terms of the heart rate level required for the athlete during the warm up. If you were to use the 70 percent VO_2 max level suggested earlier, you would need to warm up with a heart rate of between 78 percent (ACSM) and 83 percent (Marshall University) of your maximum heart rate.

Taking an average of the ACSM and the Marshall University numbers, we can suggest that a 60 to 70 percent VO_2 max warm up would be

ACSM % of Max heart rate	ACSM VO$_2$	Max Marshall Univ. study % of Max heart rate
55	40	63
70	60	76
85	80	89
90	85	92

Reprinted from Chapter 11. D.P. Swain, K.S. Abernathy, C.S. Smith, S.J. Lee and S. A. Bunn. "Target heart rates for the development of cardiorespiratory fitness." *Medicine and Science in Sports and Exercise* 26:1 (1994): 112-116)

about 73 to 80 percent of the maximum heart rate level of 220 minus the athlete's age multiplied by .70 to .80. For a 20 year old, this would be a 140 to 160 level of heart rate for 15 minutes. We might infer that this would be an effective warm up for sprinters, but it might take too much energy from distance runners.

Recommended cool down

After the practice or a competition, stretching might not hurt, but excessive stretching might set up the muscle fibers for injury during the next practice. There is no evidence that post-exercise stretching will increase flexibility or reduce delayed onset muscle soreness, yet these were the reasons given for our stretching after a workout or competition. Stretching for an increased range of motion should have been done very early in the sports season immediately after the last season, in fact.

> ### Warm-up
> For most people: no stretching.
>
> Warm up the muscle actively: from slow to faster movements.

Some post-exercise jogging might assist in reducing the blood pooling in the muscles, but if bruises, strains or sprains were incurred in the practice or competition, the extra work might increase the blood flow to the injury and increase the swelling when it should have been treated with ice or cold to reduce any potential swelling.

There have been few studies on the effects of cool down. A study in Japan of older cardiac patients (50 to 70 years old) found that after a maximal cardiac exercise, those who used a cool down period rather than just resting had a more efficient return to normal in terms of breathing. The resting group hyperventilated and had a more uneven return to the resting state.[24]

In a 16-week Dutch study using more than 300 runners, half were given information on preventing running injuries, including how to warm up, stretch and cool down. A diary noting what was done and how many injuries occurred was kept by each runner. Those who received the information had 5.5 injuries per 1000 hours of running. Those who did not get the information had 4.9 injuries per 1000 hours of running.[25] The conclusion of the study was that the information was the first step in preventing injuries, but perhaps the study's assumption that warm up, stretching and cool down will prevent injuries is wrong or at least wrong for most runners.

Notes

1. Gleim, G.W. and M.P. McHugh. "Flexibility and its effects on sports injury and performance." *Sports Medicine* [New Zealand] 24:5 (1997): 289-299.

2. Shrier, I. "Stretching before exercise does not reduce the risk of local muscle injury: a critical review of the clinical and basic science literature." *Clinical Journal of Sports Medicine* 9:4 (1999):221-7.

3. Pope, R.P., R.D. Herbert, J.D. Kirwan, B.J. Graham. "A randomized trial of preexercise stretching for prevention of lower-limb injury." *Medicine and Science in Sports Exercise.* 32:2 (2000): 271-7.

4. Kerner, J. A. and J.C. D'Amico. "A statistical analysis of a group of runners." *Journal of the American Podiatry Association.* 73:3 (1983): 160-164.

5. Jacobs, S.J. and B.L.Berson. "Injuries to runners: a study of entrants to a 10,000 meter race." *American Journal of Sports Medicine.* 14:2 (1986): 151-155.

6. Walter, S.D. et al. "The Ontario cohort study of running-related injuries." *Archives of Internal Medicine.* 149:11 (1989): 2561-2564.

7. Johansson, P.H., L. Lindstrom, G. Sundelin, B. Lindstrom. "The effects of preexercise stretching on muscular soreness, tenderness and force loss following heavy eccentric exercise." *Scandinavian Journal of Medicine and Science in Sports.* 9:4 (1999): 219-25.

8. Gullick, D.T. "Effects of various treatment techniques on the signs and symptoms of delayed onset muscle soreness." Ph.D. thesis from Temple University, 1995.

9. Rodenburg, J. et al. "Warm up, stretching and massage diminish harmful effects of eccentric exercise" *International Journal of Sports Medicine* 15:7 (1994): 414-419.

10. High, D., E. Howley. "The effects of static stretching and warm up on prevention of delayed onset muscle soreness." *Research Quarterly for Exercise and Sports.* 60:4 (1989): 357-361.

11. Cornelius, W.L., M.R. Hands. "The effects of a warm up on acute

hip joint flexibility using a modified PNF stretching technique." *Journal of Athletic Training*. 27:2 (1992): 112-114.

12. Wilson, G. *Applied Resistance Training: A Scientific Approach*. Southern Cross University, NSW, Australia, 1998, Ch. 9, p. 25. Unpublished manuscript.

13. Young,W and S. Elliott. "Acute effects of static stretching, proprioceptive neuromuscular facilitation stretching, and maximum voluntary contractions on explosive force production and jumping performance." *Research Quarterly for Exercise and Sport*. 72:3 (2001): 273-279.

14. Shrier, I. and K. Gossal. "Myths and truths about stretching." *Physician & Sports Medicine*. 28:8 (2000): 57-63.

15. Rosenbaum, D., E.M. Hennig. "The influence of stretching and warm up exercises on Achilles tendon reflex activity." *Journal of Sports Science* 13:6 (1995):481-90.

16. Nosaka, K., P.M. Clarkson. "Influence of previous concentric exercise on eccentric exercise-induced muscle damage." *Journal of Sports Science*. 15:5 (1997): 477-83.

17. Mohr, K.J., M.M. Pink, C. Elsner, R.S. Kvitne. "Electromyographic investigation of stretching: the effect of warm up." *Clinical Journal of Sports Medicine* 8:3 (1998): 215-20.

18. Nioka, S., D. Moser, G. Lech, M. Evengelisti, T. Verde, B. Chance, S. Kuno. "Muscle deoxygenation in aerobic and anaerobic exercise." *Adv Exp Med Biol*. 454 (1998): 63-70.

19. O'Brien, B., W. Payne, P. Gastin, C. Burge. "A comparison of active and passive warm ups on energy system contribution and performance in moderate heat." *Aust J Sci Med Sport* (1997).

20. Stewart, I.B., G.G. Sleivert. "The effect of warm up intensity on range of motion and anaerobic performance." *Journal of Orthopaedic Sports Physical Therapy*. 27:2 (1998):154-61, 29:4 (1998):106-9.

21. Chesler, R.M., D.W. Michielli, M. Aron, R.A. Stein. "Cardiovascular response to sudden strenuous exercise: an exercise echocardiographic study." *Medicine and Science in Sports and Exercise*. 29:10 (1997): 1299-303.

22. Mandengue, S.H., G. Atchou, S.L. Etoundi-Ngoa, P. Tsala-Mbala "Effects of preliminary muscular exercise on body temperature, water loss and physical performance." *Sante* 6:6 (1996): 393-6.

23. Volianitis, S., A.K. McConnell, Y. Koutedakis, D.A. Jones. "The influence of prior activity upon inspiratory muscle strength in rowers and non-rowers." *International Journal of Sports Medicine* 20:8 (1999): 542-7.

24. Koyama, Y., A. Koike, T. Yajima, H. Kano, F. Marumo, M. Hiroe "Effects of 'cool-down' during exercise recovery on cardiopulmonary systems in patients with coronary artery disease." *Jpn Circ J.* 64:3 (2000): 191-6.

25. van Mechelen, W., H. Hlobil, H.C. Kemper, W.J. Voorn, H.R. de Jongh. "Prevention of running injuries by warm up, cool-down, and stretching exercises." *American Journal of Sports Medicine* 21:5 (1993): 711-9.

5

DEVELOPING
AEROBIC FITNESS

itness means that a woman is able to perform her normal daily activities with adequate energy and still have the vigor to perform additional activities. If a woman can finish the daily chores of a job, schoolwork or housekeeping, and return home with the energy necessary to play tennis, jog or work on a hobby, a minimal level of fitness has been achieved. The higher one's level of fitness, the greater the reserve of energy throughout the day will be.

The physical effects of exercising for endurance (aerobic fitness) are many. It benefits every body organ. The major emphases of exercise have correctly been focused on the benefits to the heart and circulatory system. But it should be noted that the bones and ligaments, the digestive and excretory systems and the lymphatic and respiratory systems all benefit.

The well-conditioned person is not only able to ward off infectious diseases and cancers better than the poorly conditioned person (because of a strengthened immune system), but the chances of developing heart disease, strokes, diabetes, osteoporosis and other types of degenerative and chronic diseases are also lessened.

Most people can do some type of fitness activity. A large number of paraplegics now compete in marathons, often going faster in their wheelchairs than the runners. Pete Strudley of California has run marathons without feet. His six-hour marathons are run on pads placed over the stumps at his ankle. San Franciscan Larry Lewis used to run six miles through Golden Gate Park every day on his way to work as a waiter at the Mark Hopkins Hotel. He did this until he was well over 100 years old. (He died from cancer at 106.) Up to the time of his death, he still claimed the record for the 100-yard dash for men over 100. He was able to run 100 yards in about 17 seconds when he was 100 years old. So, there is no excuse for not exercising, and most of us can do it on our feet.

A recent Dutch study used 20 sedentary men and 14 sedentary women, trained them by walking and running them three or four times a week for nine months, culminated with the running of a half-marathon (13

CHECKLIST FOR PHYSICAL FITNESS

The elements of physical fitness should be understood by anyone considering pursuing an effective path toward fitness. These elements are:
- ☐ *Flexibility* — the ability to move the joints of the body through a wide range of motion.
- ☐ *Strength* — the ability to lift a weight one time.
- ☐ *Endurance or stamina* — the ability to perform a certain task for a long period of time.
- ☐ *Agility* — the ability of the body to exhibit coordinated muscular movements.

Everyone should possess a minimum acceptable level of endurance, adequate strength to live her chosen lifestyle and sufficient flexibility to be able to move freely and to have an acceptably good posture.

---

miles) found significant changes in their bodies as a result of their training. The men lost an average of five pounds and the women two-and-a-half pounds. The men had significant reductions in their total cholesterol, their low-density lipoproteins (LDL — the most dangerous of the cholesterols) and their triglycerides. All are highly associated with heart attack risk.[1] The reduction in risk factors was much greater in the men than in the women, but this is partially accounted for by the females' hormones, which reduce the female risk until menopause.

The benefits of exercise to a society and its economy have been recognized by the governments in China, Japan and Russia. In those countries, exercise breaks often take the place of coffee or tea breaks. Many U.S. companies are developing exercise programs to increase the physical and mental health of their employees and to increase their longevity. Such programs have been shown to increase job performance by making people less prone to errors, enhancing their productivity and decreasing days missed because of illness.

MENTAL BENEFITS OF EXERCISE

The mental and emotional effects of exercise have been observed by athletes, psychologists and physiologists. Athletes generally show higher-than-average levels of social maturity, self-confidence and intellectual efficiency. The question is: Did the athletic activity actually develop these qualities or were they already present? And were they instrumental in the decision to become an athlete?

A study at Purdue University showed that untrained middle-aged university employees significantly improved their mental outlooks dur-

ADVANTAGES OF AEROBIC EXERCISE

☐ More general physical endurance because:
- The heart becomes stronger and can transmit more blood with each beat (stroke volume)
- More red blood cells are produced and carried in the blood, which makes each unit of blood a more effective carrier of oxygen to the tissues. These allow a slower heart rate with more rest between beats for the heart. (A heart beating 80 beats per minute beats 115,000 times per day; at 50 beats per minute the heart beats 72,000 times per day, a savings of 43,000 beats per day.)
- More blood flow to the muscles used during exercise (muscular endurance).
- More strength in muscles used.
- Better blood circulation to the heart muscle.
- More effective sleep and rest patterns

☐ Better resistance to disease because:
- The immune factors increase, reducing the chances of cancers, colds and other illnesses.
- Increased burning of sugars, making insulin less needed (for diabetics).
- Decreased triglycerides and low-density cholesterols, which are risk factors in heart attacks.
- Lower blood pressure, which reduces heart attack risk.
- Controlled weight, which reduces the risk of heart disease and diabetes.
- Decrease in body fat.
- Stronger bones, so less chance of osteoporosis.

☐ Better psychological health
- Increase of endorphins, which are natural brain stimulants.
- Reduction in tensions felt.
- Decrease in the effects of stresses and depression.
- Increased self-esteem due to:
  1. Accomplishing a worthwhile fitness activity
  2. Improving one's appearance (better posture, reduced body fat)

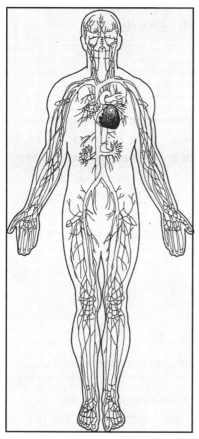

As you get in better condition, your circulatory system becomes more efficient. Your small blood vessels enlarge and your heart becomes more efficient.

ing the course of a specially designed fitness program of calisthenics and jogging. Results showed significant positive changes had occurred. The areas of self-assurance, stability and imagination were all greatly improved in the test subjects. The circulation of blood to the brain during exercise aids in making one more alert. Physical activity during an exercise can also make one more relaxed.

Another reason for exercising aerobically is that we look better when we exercise effectively. And when we look good, we feel good. This aesthetic value of exercise, combined with some diet changes, is just another good reason to be fit.

THE ADVANTAGES APPLY EQUALLY TO WOMEN AND MEN

Old notions that exercise is unfeminine have been dispelled. The fascinatingly feminine Olga Korbut of the Soviet gymnastics team captured the hearts of the world in the 1972 Olympics. Then, Nadia Comaneci of Romania did it again in 1976. Florence Griffith-Joyner of the United States did it again in 1988 when she ran away from the field in the sprints. (Griffith-Joyner died in 1998 of a rare heart disease not related to her sport.) 2000 Olympic javelin champion and world record holder Trine Hattestad of Norway shares her joys and successes with her husband and her two children, 10 and 3.

It has finally been recognized by the medical profession and the Olympic Committee that women can do anything that men can do. This idea has filtered to the general population, where we now see women running, lifting weights and playing soccer and water polo, in addition to the sports they have traditionally done — swimming, tennis, gymnastics and riding.

The fears of some women that exercise would make them too muscular have proven unfounded. The fact is that exercise aids in slimming the figure to conform to the bone structure of the natural female anatomy. Exercise can flatten the abdomen, remove excess fat, firm the muscles and assist in the development of a more attractive posture.

A study of 40,000 women in Minnesota aged 55 to 69 showed that as little as one day a week of exercise significantly reduced death rates. The more physical activity they got and the more vigorous it was, the lower the death rates.[2] Maintaining good physical conditioning can aid women in reducing most of the diseases of aging. Exercise also often aids in relieving menstrual discomforts. The high body heat and the increased circulation that occurs during exercise aid in relieving the congestion of blood in the uterus, a major cause of discomfort.

A Harvard University study found that female runners produced a less potent form of estrogen than did their nonexercising counterparts. This was held to be a factor in the 50 percent reduction of expected cases of breast and cervical cancers and a 65 percent reduction in a type of diabetes that is more common among women than men.

AGE AND EXERCISE

Age is a factor in choosing the types and amounts of exercise one should do. A person who has been exercising regularly will be *younger* than a person who has not been exercising. That is, the condition of the person's body — its biological age — will be less than that expected for that person's chronological age. While for the average person's conditioning level (scientifically called the VO_2 max) reduces about one percent per year after age 25, a well-conditioned person can slow or even reverse that normal process of aging.

If someone has not done much exercise, the body might become physiologically older than its chronological age would indicate. The bones can be softer, the blood pressure higher, the amount of artery hardening greater, the blood supply less, the digestive processes slower and many other factors that we associate with age can be present. But if that same person were to begin an effective exercise program, those results of aging can be slowed, stopped and reversed.

Osteoporosis (porous bones), an affliction of many older women and some thin men, can be prevented or reversed by weight-bearing exercise. Walking or running, weightlifting or calisthenics can all prevent its development. Swimming, while an effective endurance exercise, does not prevent the disease because the water, not the person's body, supports the weight.

Exercise can make you feel better and live longer no matter when you begin your program. If you begin when you are young and continue the program, you might add years to your life and life to your years. But you are never too old to begin. It seems that exercise might be the next best thing to the fountain of youth.

The National Institute on Aging, Gerontology Research Center, in Baltimore, Maryland, has done a 25-year study on aging men and women and the loss of strength and power (a combination of speed and strength). At about age 40, both strength and power declined in both sexes. However, power declined faster than strength in men.[3] With the loss of muscle cells and the reduction of physical work, we can expect that strength will decrease. But many of us want to keep that loss minimal by exercising for strength and power.

Endurance activities can be continued throughout life or can begin as we get older. A number of people participate in Masters-level competitions. These competitions usually begin in the 30- to 40-year age range and can go to the 90- to 100-year age group. There are competitions in walking, running, swimming, orienteering, rowing, cycling, volleyball and nearly every other sport one can imagine. In the Canadian study previously cited (Shephard), during the seven-year follow-up of the 750 respondents (aged 40 to 81 with an average age of 58), far fewer than expected had developed a serious illness over the study period. Most had given up smoking before or during their training period. Only 2.9 percent still smoked, while 32.8 percent were former smokers. The participants were shown to have been more interested in their health than the general population, as shown by their increased use of seat belts when driving and a greater propensity to see a doctor if something seemed wrong. And more important, their outlooks were happier and their lives seemed more fulfilling.

ENDURANCE AND STAMINA

Stamina is developed by exercises that make the heart beat fast over a relatively long period of time. This is the most important aspect of physical fitness. While everyone gains benefits from exercising, some gain their benefits faster. They are *high responders* to their training. These are the people who are more likely to become the competitive runners and walkers.

Most of us have the minimum level of flexibility and strength we need to live our lives effectively. We generally have enough sugar in our blood or fat in our bodies to give us fuel for energy. However, we often lack the ability to exercise at a level beyond that which is our norm.

The more common physiological terms for endurance are either cardiovascular (heart-blood) or cardiorespiratory (heart-lung function) endurance. Those who have developed such fitness have trained their bodies to use oxygen efficiently. Since oxygen is just as important in developing energy as is blood sugar, but cannot be stored like sugar, the ability to use oxygen effectively must be developed.

Very few people function at even the most minimal fitness levels. Yet, proper exercise for as little as 30 minutes each day can make one's body function better, control obesity, strengthen the bones, reduce mental tensions, and reduce one's chances of heart and blood circulation problems. For one's physical and mental health, for a chance to live a longer and happier life, there is probably no better investment of time than a daily dose of proper endurance exercise.

If you don't like walking or running in inclement weather, a bicycle exerciser can be your answer to continued conditioning.

Most national medical associations as well as the surgeon general have now taken this position: "Exercise is the most significant factor contributing to the health of the individual." Study after study indicates that proper endurance exercise is a major factor in increasing the chances of living a longer life. A study of more than 17,000 British executives showed that those who exercised vigorously had only one-third the risk of developing a fatal disease during middle age than light exercisers or nonexercisers.

The effects of cardiovascular endurance exercise on the circulatory system are:

- The red blood cells become more numerous. These are the cells that carry oxygen from the lungs to the muscles and other tissues of the body. The increase in these blood cells enables each beat of the heart to carry more oxygen to the tissues.
- The number of blood vessels being used in the muscles is increased. This gives the muscles more capacity for using the oxygen that is brought to them in the blood.
- The heart might enlarge, enabling it to pump more blood in less time to the muscles and tissues that need it. The enlarged heart beats slower than a normal heart when resting; it has a longer rest period between each beat. An athletically enlarged heart generally occurs only with those who have been dedicated endurance athletes.

The *heart* is really a double pump. One pump (the right heart) receives *used* blood that has just come from the body after delivering nutrients and oxygen to the body tissues. The blood is received into the right atrium (Latin for room), the top chamber of the right side of the heart. It is then pumped into the right ventricle, where the next heart beat pumps this dark, bluish-red blood to the lungs, where the blood gets rid of a waste gas (carbon dioxide) and picks up a fresh supply of oxygen that turns it a bright red again. The second pump (the left side of the heart) receives this *reconditioned* blood from the lungs in the left atrium. The next beat pushes the newly oxygenated blood into the heavily muscled left ventricle. The next beat pumps the blood out through the great trunk artery (aorta) to be distributed by smaller arteries to all parts of the body.

The heart is a very strong pump. Each day, it pumps about 13 tons of blood. Each minute, it pumps the total volume of the body's blood through the circulatory system. During heavy exercise, it might pump the entire volume of the blood of the body nine times each minute. That's a lot of work for a 12-ounce organ.

The heart can enlarge normally when it has been forced to work hard to pump the blood of a person who exercises for long periods of time. Swimmers, basketball players and long-distance runners usually have such enlarged hearts. This normal enlargement is generally considered to be good.

Abnormal heart enlargement is found in many people for various reasons. These people's hearts have been forced to beat rapidly for reasons other than exercise. The heart of an obese person will have to beat many more times each day just to pump blood through the excess fat of that person. Some people have abnormally enlarged hearts because their heart valves do not function efficiently. Many have abnormally enlarged hearts because their arteries are clogged and narrowed, so the heart must push

---

TAKING A PULSE (HEART BEATS PER MINUTE)

1. Find the place where your pulse is felt the easiest. (Inside the muscle on the side of the neck below the left side of your jaw OR just inside your collar bone OR just above the wrist and inside the arm bone on the thumb side OR over your heart.)
2. Count your pulse for 60 seconds while resting. My resting pulse is ___ beats per minute.
3. While exercising, you can take your pulse for 15 seconds and multiply by 4 OR take it for 10 seconds and multiply by 6, BUT the most common method is taking it for 6 seconds and multiplying by 10. So, if your six-second pulse is 12, your pulse rate for a minute is 120.

the blood at a much higher pressure to get the blood to the organs and muscles. The previously mentioned heart valve damage can also cause the heart to enlarge due to the extra work that it is forced to do.

A normally enlarged heart will beat slower than normal as it enlarges. An abnormally enlarged heart will generally continue to beat relatively fast since it has enlarged because of extreme stresses. Its enlargement would allow more blood to be pumped with each beat. But because of the great demands of the body (such as in obesity) or in the heart's inefficiency (such as damaged valves), enlargement is not enough. The heart must therefore continue to beat at a relatively fast rate.

The *pulse rate* is the number of heartbeats per minute. The average person's heart beats 70 to 80 times per minute when the person is at rest. However, the better conditioned the person is, the lower the pulse rate. Some athletes have pulse rates in the 30s. A pulse rate of 50 would be very good for the average person. A former Swedish tennis star had a pulse rate of 28. This was achieved because of the way he practiced, continually running while hitting for several hours every day.

There are several methods of finding your pulse rate. First, you must find an artery that is near the surface of the skin. The most common places are just inside the muscle at the side of the neck near the jaw, at the base of the neck just inside the collar bone, the inside of the wrist about two inches below the base of the thumb, or directly over the heart. Place the fingers — not the thumb — of one hand on one of these spots. If your fingers are at the correct place, you will feel a throbbing. Each throb is a pulsation of blood from the heart. Count the number of beats for one minute. Or count the number of beats for 15 seconds and multiply by four. This will give you your resting pulse rate in beats per minute. If you are exercising, you might count for six seconds, then multiply by 10 to get your pulse rate for 60 seconds. One's pulse is always measured in beats per minute.

A heart that beats 70 times per minute has one-half second to fill with blood. This resting phase is called the diastolic period. If the pulse rate is increased to 120 beats per minute, the resting phase is reduced to one-fourth of a second. In spite of the shorter resting phase, the heart still remains functional to about 160 beats per minute. At that point, the resting phase might be so short that the right atrium of the heart cannot fill completely with blood and each beat might pump less blood.

Even though the resting phase of the heart is diminished when it beats faster, there are other things that happen to keep the heart efficient. The blood pressure increases, which pushes more blood into the heart. As the muscles contract, they might be massaging the veins. This aids in a more rapid return of blood to the heart. The blood becomes more acidic due to the lactic acid formed in the muscles as a result of the use of sugars for energy. This acidic quality enhances the ability of the hemoglobin in the red blood cells to pick up the oxygen in the lungs. These factors enable the heart to pump four to 10 times as much blood during heavy exercise as during rest.

The well-conditioned person's heart gets more resting periods than does the heart of the person in average condition. If a person's heart were to beat 20 times less per minute (i.e., 60 rather than 80 beats per minute), it would save nearly 10,000 beats during a night's sleep and nearly 30,000 beats in a 24-hour day. It would get 18 days per year more rest than the heart with the higher pulse rate.

Red blood cells carry the oxygen from the lungs to the body tissues by means of an iron compound called *hemoglobin*. These red blood cells are 1/3500 of an inch in diameter. They are formed in the bone marrow and live about three months. When red cells are destroyed, the body reclaims most of the iron and uses it to form new red cells. A diet that is deficient in iron will probably cause anemia (a lack of red cells). Menstruating women have nearly double the need for daily iron intake than do other women or men.

The more blood and red cells present in each unit of blood, the greater the oxygen-carrying capacity of the blood. If a person lives high above sea level, the body's need for oxygen increases. This is because the air at high altitudes is less dense, so there is less oxygen per cubic foot of air. The body then manufactures more red blood cells so that a greater proportion of the oxygen in the air is absorbed. The Aymara Indians of the Andes Mountains have an average red cell blood count of eight million per cubic centimeter of blood. The average person at sea level has a red cell count of about 4.5 million. Strenuous exercise and high-altitude living have the same effect on the red cell count. As the body's need for oxygen increases, the red blood cells increase to accommodate that need if the diet contains sufficient iron.

Exercise also increases the total amount of blood in the body. The average person can increase the total amount of blood by 10 to 20 percent during 10 weeks of effective endurance training. This can increase the blood volume by up to two quarts. Well-trained athletes might have more than 40 percent more blood circulating in their bodies than do average people. This means that the heart doesn't have to pump as often to get the needed oxygen to the muscles and other tissues because each spoonful of blood carries more red cells and, consequently, more oxygen.

The condition of the muscles is another factor in endurance. Only the muscles that are specifically involved in an activity will gain endurance.

The legs of a long-distance runner or cyclist and the chest and upper-back muscles of a swimmer will show marked changes when they become well-conditioned. The number of small blood vessels (capillaries) being used by the muscle will increase so that more blood will be able to circulate through the muscle. This allows more oxygen and blood sugars to be available for energy. Endurance exercise will also change the type of muscle fiber, making more of the fibers the type that can utilize oxygen more effectively.

HOW MUCH EXERCISE DO I NEED?

In the past, we have looked upon fitness as a maximum level of cardiovascular endurance. It required increasing the heart rate significantly for 30 minutes a day in running, walking, swimming or doing other such endurance activities. This was based on the earlier aerobic theories of Dr. Ken Cooper, which were refined at Stanford University, then adopted by the American Academy of Sports Medicine. The standard required starting with a maximum heart rate of 220 beats per minute, then adjusting it for age by subtracting your age to get the maximum heart rate for your age. We were advised to exercise at a rate of 45/55 to 90 percent of that age-adjusted maximum heart rate for 20 to 30 minutes at least three or four times a week. Some experts have now increased that range from 60 to 90 percent of one's maximum heart rate. The higher number is for the better-conditioned athletes.

In the 1990s, Dr. Steve Blair, the primary epidemiologist at Dr. Cooper's Aerobic Research Institute in Dallas, Texas, developed a new theory. Based on his analysis of 25,000 men who had been examined at the institute, he suggested that getting a half-hour a day of some sort of exercise is enough to extend one's life. That exercise does not have to be done all at one time. You can walk five minutes in the morning, garden for 15 minutes later in the day, climb stairs for 30 seconds, then walk for 10 minutes later in the day. This accumulated exercise indicated an increase in lifespan was more easily obtainable. Such exercise seems to be more important than being overweight. (Being obese is another matter.) It even reduces the risks of smoking.[4] Dr. Blair is the former president of the American College of Sports Medicine and is perhaps the world's most respected authority in the area of fitness and death risk.

While the accumulation of 30 minutes a day of low-level exercise will increase your lifespan, it seems that a more vigorous exercise program will reduce death risks and increase the health benefits far more. Therefore, the American College of Sports Medicine has reevaluated its position. (Its present position was developed in 1999 and can be accessed on the Internet at www.ASCM.org. It is briefly incorporated in this and

SOME HELPFUL DEFINITIONS
Aerobic: using air (oxygen) as a primary source of energy. If exercising hard, air is the primary factor in developing your energy potential. It becomes the major source of energy after about 30 seconds.
Anaerobic: the early part of exercise is fueled by body chemicals (ATP and creatine) not oxygen. It is generally the major source of energy for the first 30 seconds of hard exercise.

other chapters of this book.) The importance of aerobic exercise is probably the reason that both Dr. Cooper and Dr. Blair run several miles nearly every day. It seems that for maximum fitness, the earlier idea of 30 minutes a day of a significant raise in pulse rate still seems ideal, if not minimal. This will be examined later in the chapter.

Dr. Blair's findings have now been somewhat modified and call for a higher expenditure of energy — about 40 to 60 percent of one's maximum activity potential, the VO_2 max. This would require walking briskly for 1½ to 2 miles for 30 minutes each day. It could be done in three 10-minute segments but is slightly better if done all at once. This is considered to be a minimum fitness level for sedentary people. So, more — either a higher intensity of exercise or a longer duration of activity — is certainly better.[5]

Another factor that you might consider is that exercising more than 30 minutes a day at a high pulse rate continues to decrease your risk of heart disease. Exercising up to an hour continues to reduce your heart risk. However, more than 60 minutes of exercise does not seem to reduce the risk of heart disease significantly more than the 60-minute workout. More than 60 minutes would burn more calories and contribute to weight loss. It would also reduce the risk of some types of diabetes. However, the wear and tear on the joints from running might be a negative risk factor for those who do too much jogging. So, more than a half-hour a day of exercise should only be done if it is enjoyable and does not cause any physical pain.

An American study[6] suggests a weekly output of 2000 calories in exercise in order to achieve a minimal level of fitness. This would require five hours of exercise per week with an expenditure of eight calories per minute.

EXERCISING FOR BETTER AEROBIC FITNESS

Effective aerobic exercise, according to The American College of Sports Medicine (ACSM) report of 1999, requires that aerobic exercise be done three to five times per week for 20 to 60 minutes each session at an intensity of 45/55 to 90 percent of maximum heart rate or 50 to 85 percent of maximal oxygen consumption (VO_2 max). (In addition, the ACSM recommends the inclusion of a strength-training program for overall health benefits.) It should be noted that the 45 to 55 percent maximum heart-rate level is for people who are in poor physical condition. Athletes should be near the 90 percent level and the rest of us should be in the 60 to 80 percent range.

As mentioned earlier, you should determine your target heart rate zone (where your heart rate should be while exercising to increase cardiorespiratory fitness). The simpler calculation is the older standard used by the ACSM. To do this, you must first determine your maximal heart rate. This is done by subtracting your age from 220. Then, you can determine the limits of your intensity by multiplying your maximal heart rate by between .6 and .9. (The higher number is for better-conditioned people.) For instance, if you are 50 years old, then your maximal heart rate is 220 - 50 = 170. To determine your minimal target heart rate, multiply 170 x .6 = 102 beats per minute. For the top of your target heart rate zone, multiply 170 x .9 = 153 beats per minute. Beginners should begin at the low end of the target heart rate range and slowly increase their exercising heart rate as their body adapts to the increased physical demands of exercise.

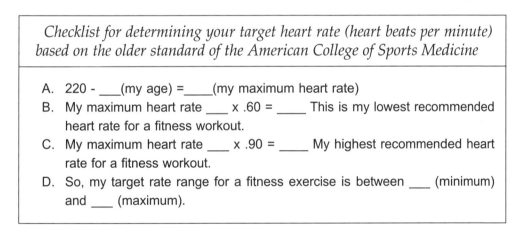

Checklist for determining your target heart rate (heart beats per minute) based on the older standard of the American College of Sports Medicine

A. 220 - ___ (my age) = ____ (my maximum heart rate)
B. My maximum heart rate ___ x .60 = ____ This is my lowest recommended heart rate for a fitness workout.
C. My maximum heart rate ___ x .90 = ____ My highest recommended heart rate for a fitness workout.
D. So, my target rate range for a fitness exercise is between ___ (minimum) and ___ (maximum).

Scientists are continuing to improve their knowledge of how best our bodies can work. The Finnish scientist Karvonen has improved on the simple formula of 220 minus your age as the maximum heart rate. He starts with that number but then subtracts the resting pulse rate to determine the *heart rate reserve*. This formula is more generally used today and gives a slightly higher target heart rate for most people.

1. First, subtract your age from 220. This is your *maximum heart rate* (MHR). Next, you will need to determine your *resting pulse rate*. Take this while lying in bed in the morning before you get up. Use your index and middle fingers and locate your pulse either

on the side of your neck (carotid artery) or on the wrist just above the thumb. Count the number of pulse beats in a minute or take your pulse for 15 seconds and multiply by four to determine the total number of beats in a minute.

2. Resting heart (pulse) rate (Rest HR) ___

3. Subtract the resting pulse rate from the maximum pulse rate. Answer for the first question: subtract the answer for the second. This gives your heart-rate reserve.

    MHR ___ - Rest HR ___ = ___ heart rate reserve (HRR)

    Now, you will determine your maximum and minimum pulse rates for an effective workout. For the average person your high end will be your heart-rate reserve multiplied by 80 percent (.8) then add to that number your resting pulse rate.

4. ___ (HRR) x .80 = ___ + ___ (Rest HR) = ___ Maximum desirable heart rate during exercise.

    Next, find the minimal acceptable level for your workout by taking the heart-rate reserve, multiplying it by 60 percent (.6), then adding in your resting pulse rate.

    ___ (HRR) x .60 = ___ + ___ (Rest HR)= ___ Minimal desirable heart rate during exercise.

These two percentages — 60 percent and 80 percent — are not set in stone. If you have medical problems or are in very poor condition, you might use a number between 40 and 55 percent to set your minimal pulse rate. If you are very fit or a competitive athlete, you might use 85 or 90 percent to set your high-end exercise pulse rate.

Using Karvonen's formula, or the heart-rate reserve concept of aerobic fitness, the ASCM's recommendations are for 40/50 to 85 percent of this formula for a fitness target. So, whether you use the older standard of 220 minus your age (maximum heart rate standard) or the more complicated Karvonen formula, the equivalent fitness levels can be ascertained, with the Karvonen formula requiring about a five percent lower percentage of the maximum heart rate than is needed for the maximum heart rate standard.

Whichever formula you use, the exercise should be done for 20 to 60 minutes, with those using the lower percentages exercising longer in order to get the same gains. So, for aerobic fitness, there is a scale from high intensity (high heart rate) and shorter duration (in minutes) to the lower intensity and longer duration exercise period. Of course, athletes or serious aerobic exercisers will work at both a high intensity and longer duration in their workouts.

As you improve in your cardiorespiratory conditioning, your resting

Here is an example of how a 20-year-old would determine the target training pulse range using Karvonen's formula. Assume that her resting pulse rate is 70.

Minimum target heart rate (220-20=200-70=130). 130 x .60=78 + 70=148
Maximum target heart rate (220-20=200-70=130). 130 x .80=104 + 70=174

For a 40-year-old with a resting pulse of 65, the target heart rates would be:

Minimum target heart rate (220-40=180-65=115) 115 x .60=69 + 70=139
Maximum target heart rate (220-40=180-65=115) 115 x .80=92 + 65=157

heart rate will drop. While the average male pulse rate is 72 and the average women's pulse is 78, it doesn't take long to drop those levels with effective endurance training. It is quite easy to get into the 60 or even the 50 level for resting pulse rates. But this higher level of fitness requires more than walking a few minutes a day and doing some gardening.

Physiologists use another measure to determine cardiorespiratory fitness. The VO_2 max (maximum volume of oxygen) is the major physiological measurement used by exercise physiologists. It determines the amount of oxygen that a body can use to develop energy while exercising. (The maximum amount of oxygen used [VO_2 max] is the number of milliliters [ml] of oxygen [O_2] per kilogram of body weight per minute.)

DETERMINING YOUR FITNESS LEVEL USING THE ROCKPORT FITNESS WALKING TEST

1. Measure out one mile on either an indoor or outdoor surface.
2. Walk as fast as possible throughout the mile.
3. Record the time it takes you to walk the mile.
4. Record your heart rate immediately upon completion of the mile walk. This can be easily and quickly done by taking your heart rate for:
   a. 6 seconds and multiplying that number by 10
   b. 10 seconds and multiplying that number by 6
   c. 15 seconds and multiplying that number by 4
5. Determine what your mile time is in minutes and hundredths of a minute. For instance, if your walk time was 10 minutes, 15 seconds = 10.25. This is the number you will plug into the formulas on the next page.
6. Find the appropriate chart for your age and sex. Pinpoint the spot on the top of the chart that indicates your time for the mile walk. Draw a vertical line down from that spot. Then find the spot on the left side of the chart that corresponds with your pulse rate at the finish of your walk. Draw a horizontal line across the chart from that spot. Where the lines intersect is the zone that indicates your level of conditioning.

ROCKPORT FITNESS WALKING TEST: ESTIMATING YOUR VO₂ MAX FROM YOUR ONE MILE WALK

1. Measure out one mile on either an indoor or outdoor surface.
2. Walk as fast as possible throughout the mile.
3. Record the time it takes you to walk the mile.
4. Record your heart rate immediately upon completion of the mile walk. This can be easily and quickly done by taking your heart rate for:
   a. 6 seconds and multiplying that number by 10
   b. 10 seconds and multiplying that number by 6
   c. 15 seconds and multiplying that number by 4
5. Determine what your mile time is in minutes and hundredths of a minute. For instance, if your walk time was 10 minutes, 15 seconds = 10.25. This is the number you will plug into the following formulas.
6. Use the following gender-specific formulas to determine maximal oxygen consumption rates (VO₂ max).

MALE	FEMALE
_____ = 0.0947 x body weight	_____ = 0.0585 x body weight
_____ = 0.3709 x age	_____ = 0.3885 x age
_____ = 3.9744 x mile time	_____ = 2.7961 x mile time
_____ = 0.1847 x mile heart rate	_____ = 0.1109 x mile heart rate

7. Add these four numbers together. Put that number here _____.
8. For men, take 154.899 and subtract the number you found in step 7 to determine your VO₂ max. 154.899 - _____ = _____ VO₂ max
9. For women, take 116.579 and subtract the number you found in step 7 to determine your VO₂ max. 116.579 - _____ = _____ VO₂ max

THE MILE WALK TEST (Developed by Dr. James Rippe of the University of Massachusetts)

1. Find a quarter-mile track at a school or measure a mile with the odometer of your car. (You can also measure a half-mile, walk the half-mile then walk back to the starting point.)
2. Time yourself or have somebody else time you for the mile walk.
3. Evaluate yourself against the following criteria:

Fitness level	Males (minutes:seconds)	Females (minutes:seconds)
Excellent	Less than 10:12	Less than 11:40
Good	10:13 to 11:42	11:41 to 13:08
Average	11:43 to 13:13	13:09 to 14:36
Low Average	13:14 to 14:44	14:37 to 16:04
Below Average	14:45 to 16:23	16:05 to 17:31
Poor	More than 16:23	More than 17:31

Males generally have about a 20 percent higher average VO_2 max than females. Age also influences it. A 20-year-old male will probably average 50, a 40-year-old will probably drop to 40 and a 70-year-old will score a 30. The top-conditioned athlete in the world has a 95 VO_2 max. While you will never get to that 95 level of conditioning, you can certainly improve your own level through exercise.

To estimate your maximal oxygen consumption rate (VO_2 max), you can do the Rockport Fitness Walking Test [7], as this has been validated by the ACSM as an appropriate fitness test.

Now that you know your maximal oxygen consumption, you can test to see whether your cardiorespiratory fitness program is working by occasionally repeating the above test. As your fitness level increases, your VO_2 max will increase because cardiorespiratory fitness relies on the effective delivery and use of oxygen to make energy.

BEGINNING A CARDIOVASCULAR FITNESS PROGRAM

If you are in poor or average condition and desire to increase your fitness level, be sure that you begin with a low-intensity activity such as walking or use a low-intensity level on a stationary bike or a stair climber. Whichever approach you choose, start slowly. If you begin any exercise program too quickly, you will probably have some muscle soreness for the first few days. This soreness discourages some people, but it will disappear and will probably never return as you get into condition and keep fit.

Keep improving by gradually increasing the amount of time spent exercising and/or the intensity at which you exercise. Eventually, you will reach your fitness objectives. When you reach these objectives, you can continue to work at that level for maintenance.

Just about any time of day is a good time to exercise. However, if you exercise just before you go to bed, you will increase your metabolism, which might make it more difficult to sleep. If you exercise just after eating, you will force your body to divide the available blood between the stomach, which needs it for digestion, and the skeletal muscles, which need it for exercise. But if you exercise just before a meal, you might find that you don't desire as much food. If you use your exercise sessions to give you energy, you might choose to exercise in the morning. If you use your exercise sessions to relieve the stress and tension of your day, the evening would be a more appropriate time.

Endurance exercise requires a proper warm up, a vigorous activity period and a cool-down session. Even well-conditioned people often show abnormal electrocardiograms when they exercise without a proper warm up. However, they will show normal electrocardiograms when

MAXIMAL OXYGEN UPTAKE NORMS FOR WOMEN AND MEN (ml/kg/min)						
Relative maximal O$_2$ uptake	18-25 years old	26-35 years old	36-45 years old	46-55 years old	56-65 years old	65+ years old
	women's numbers are on top, men's below					
excellent	>56 >60	>52 >56	>45 >51	>40 >45	>37 >41	>32 >37
good	46-56 52-60	45-52 49-56	38-45 43-51	34-40 39-45	32-37 36-41	28-32 33-37
above average	42-46 47-51	39-44 43-48	34-37 39-42	31-33 35-38	28-31 32-35	25-27 29-32
average	38-41 42-46	35-38 40-42	31-33 35-38	28-30 32-35	25-27 30-31	22-24 26-28
below average	33-37 37-41	31-34 35-39	27-30 31-34	25-27 29-31	22-24 26-29	19-22 22-25
poor	28-32 30-36	26-30 30-34	22-26 26-30	20-24 25-28	18-21 22-25	17-18 20-21
very poor	<28 <30	<26 <30	<22 <26	<20 <25	<18 <22	<17 <20

they are warmed up prior to exercising. A warm up is designed to increase blood flow to the muscles you are going to work. A good indication that you are properly warmed up is when you begin to sweat. Five minutes is usually sufficient to get your body ready for your workout.

Cooling down after an exercise period is important if the exercise has been vigorous. It is suggested that the activity be slowed until the heart rate has reached a rate of about 100 beats per minute. When a person stops immediately after exercising, a great deal of blood might pool in the veins, which may decrease the amount of blood available to the brain. If a person does not cool down properly, dizziness or fainting is possible. Shock isalso a remote possibility, and even a heart attack is possible.

The best endurance exercises include walking briskly, cross-country skiing, running, swimming, aerobics, stair climbing and cycling, as well as walking on a treadmill or exercising on a bicycle exerciser. The worst

NORMS FOR 1.5 MILE RUN TEST		
Fitness Classification	Time (ages 17-25)	Time (ages 26-35)
Superior		
Male	<8:30	<9:30
Female	<10:30	<11:30
Excellent		
Male	8:30-9:29	9:30-10:29
Female	10:30-11:49	11:30-12:49
Good		
Male	9:30-10:29	10:30-11:29
Female	11:50-13:09	12:50-14:09
Moderate		
Male	10:30-11:29	11:30-12:29
Female	13:10-14:29	14:10-15:29
Fair		
Male	11:30-12:29	12:30-13:29
Female	14:30-15:49	15:30-16:49
Poor		
Male	>12:29	>13:29
Female	>15:49	>16:49

endurance exercises are weight lifting, calisthenics, archery, horseshoes and bowling, as these are of no use in developing endurance.

Fatigue is a natural byproduct of maximal muscle functioning. According to Paavo Komi, probably the world's leading muscle physiologist, muscle fatigue peaks on the second day after exhaustive exercise and is completely eliminated within four to seven days. It is caused by a combination of factors, including the buildup of chemical byproducts caused by the exercise and possible muscle and connective tissue short-term damage.[8]

Fatigue of the breathing muscles in the abdomen can cause spasms. The so-called *stitch in the side* can cause slight pain that will soon dissipate. It is generally only experienced in people who are not in good condition. The causes are unknown, but hypotheses include an increase in lactic acid buildup, not drinking enough water and overworked muscles. The most likely cause, however, is the lack of oxygen to the poorly conditioned muscles. The cramping can be reduced or eliminated by slowing your pace or stopping and breathing deeply.

MAKE IT FUN

While the subject of this book is fitness on foot you can get your exercise in many different aerobic activities. In fact, most top athletes, especially the endurance athletes, do crosstraining. While their competitive races might be in running, they might swim, cycle, ski, or do other aerobic work to develop more effective conditioning and to reduce the possible boredom of doing only one kind of activity. The 1996 Olympic 800-meter run champion lives in central Norway. Part of his winter training was to run up a snow-covered hill, then take his sled and slide down.

Effective exercise is going to make you feel better physically and mentally. This will happen whether you enjoy the exercise or not. But why not enjoy it? If you like to run, then run. If you like to play basketball, then play basketball. If you like to dance, dance. It doesn't matter if it is ballet, country-western, swing or jazz, as long as your heart rate is increased. Anything that you do physically will help a little. Walk up the stairs at work. Take a walk while you talk during your lunch break.

If you like outdoor activities, run or walk your way to fitness. These are the most common approaches to exercise. Many people are now enjoying orienteering. If you join an orienteering club, you will take your map and run or walk from point to point as the map requires. So, your brain must work along with your legs. (Orienteering will be introduced in Chapter 10.) Orienteering is becoming more and more popular. There are national and international competitions.

Running, stair climbing or cycling might be boring for you. If so, try to make it entertaining by listening to music or use a Walkman while you jog. Or you might watch television or read while you exercise indoors on some form of stationary aerobic equipment. Try to do something to make exercise enjoyable for you because the benefits you receive from it are well worth the effort!

Working out in a health studio environment is enjoyable for many people. You can lift weights with friends. You might walk or run on a treadmill while watching TV. Many health clubs also offer outside social activities, so the total program should increase the joy of exercising.

Some of us like to work out at home because it doesn't take any commuting time to go to the gym. You can jump rope, follow an aerobics program on TV or ride the exercise bike while watching TV or reading. If you want to read, you can buy a commercially made book holder that attaches to the bike's handlebars or you can rummage around the local hardware store and make your own with plastic, clamps and tape.

If you are not already exercising effectively, are you motivated to look and feel better and to live longer? How strong is your motivation? You now have the knowledge necessary to begin an effective exercise program. Has it changed your attitude? Will it change your behavior?

SAMPLE LOG BOOK FOR EVALUATING
YOUR AEROBIC CONDITIONING

Date:

Resting pulse before rising in the morning:

Distance covered:

Time exercised:

Miles per hour:

Pulse rate at start:

Pulse rate after 20 minuntes:

Pulse rate at finish:

Pulse rate five minutes later:

KEEP A LOG BOOK

You will want to keep a record of where you are now and how you improve. Record your resting pulse and your pulse during and after your workout. Record the distance covered and the time spent exercising. As you get into better condition, which will begin after your first workout, your resting pulse will begin to drop. From the 72 to 78 normal range, you will soon be in the 60s. It might take some time to get into the 50s, but it is possible over time. This will require not only effective exercise but also proper nutrition with minimum amounts of protein, iron, copper, and B vitamins. (See chapters 15 and 16.)

For a more complete fitness inventory, note how often you walk during a day, how many flights of stairs you climb, how much gardening or housework you do, etc.

Notes

1. Ponjee, G.A. et al. "Regular physical activity and changes in risk factors for coronary heart disease: a nine months prospective study." *European Journal of Clinical Chemistry and Clinical Biochemistry.* 34:6 (1996): 477-483.

2. Kushi, L.H. *Journal of American Medical Association.* 277 (1997): 1287-1292)

3. Metter, E.J., R. Conwit, J. Tobin, J.L. Fozard. "Age-associated loss of power and strength in the upper extremities in women and men." *J Gerontol A Biol Sci Med Sci.* (1997): 267-276.

4. Blair, S.N. et al. "Influences of cardiorespiratory fitness and other precursors on cardiovascular disease and all-cause mortality in

men and women." *Journal of the American Medical Association* 276 (1996): 205-210.

5. Blair, S. "Physical Activity, Fitness and Health: An Overview." A presentation at the World Congress of Sports Medicine, Orlando, FL. June 2, 1998.

6. Paffenbarger, R. S. et al. "Some interrelationships of physical activity, physiological fitness, health and longevity." In Bouchard, C. Et all. *Physical Activity in Fitness and Health*. Champaign, IL: Human Kinetics, 1993. 119-133.

7. Kline, Porcari, Hintermeister, Freedson, Ward, McCarron, Ross, and Rippe, 1987

8. Komi, P. "Neuromuscular Fatigue: Disturbed Function and Delayed Recovery After Intensive Dynamic Exercise" Keynote address at the World Congress of Sports Medicine, Orlando, FL., June 2, 1998.

6

WALKING FOR FUN AND FITNESS

The simplest and least expensive form of exercise is walking. But while it is simple, its benefits can be monumental. There are the benefits of fitness that reduce body weight and increase the efficiency of the heart, lungs and blood. There are the health benefits that enhance the immune system and reduce the chances of developing diseases from colds to cancers. There are stress-reducing benefits both from the exercise and from just being out. And there can be aesthetic feelings of exhilaration induced by the loveliness of nature as we walk over the hills, through the valleys, into the woods and by the seashore.

Walking can be accomplished at different speeds. Just strolling at a leisurely pace is about three miles per hour or 20 minutes per mile. Fitness walking would more likely be four miles per hour or a 15-minutes-per-mile pace, but the speed range is from 12- to 17-minute miles. If you get into race walking you would be going at a 12-minutes-per-mile pace or faster — five or more miles per hour. In the Olympics, men average six- to seven-minute miles and women are in the seven-minute range.

Contrary to popular opinion, you will burn more calories if you walk faster. For example, if you weigh 150 pounds and walk two miles per hour you will burn 2.8 calories per minute. But if you walk five miles per hour you will use nine calories per minute. In contrast, a 150-pound jogger moving at six miles per hour would use 11.6 calories per minute.

SHOES AND CLOTHING

Read Chapter 2 to get a better understanding of how shoes are made and what clothing to wear. Shoes are obviously your most important piece of equipment. They become more important as you walk faster or longer.

Walking shoes can reduce the stresses of impact through cushioning, especially at the heel. A highly absorbent heel insert can reduce the shock of the landing by 50 percent.[1] This type of padding can make a significant difference if you are relatively heavy, you are walking on a hard surface, you are older or you are walking very fast.

If you already have pains in your foot, leg or hip, a proper orthotic with heel cushioning can often eliminate the problem within three to six months. Walkers normally suffer very few injuries because the force of impact is relatively low.

BIOMECHANICS OF WALKING

When walking, you push off on one toe while the other heel is landing. Normally, there is more weight on the outside of the heel when it hits the ground. This force then moves across the foot; at the end of the stride, the major force is on the ball of the foot, just behind the big toe and on the big toe.

Your *heel strike* will begin your stride (see photo). Your foot will be at about a 90 percent angle to your leg and at about a 35- to 40-degree angle to the ground. As the heel hits, there will be more weight on the outside of it. You will *roll* over your foot as the weight transfers from the back of the heel to the toes as the hips move over the foot. Be sure to keep your feet pointed forward. If the toes are pointed too far out, your leg will twist outward, resulting in poor body mechanics, a shorter stride and too much weight on the big toe on the push off. If the feet are turned too far in, the leg will twist inward, resulting in not enough force being applied on the push off.

Heel strike

The *push off* should be from well behind the hips. Taking an early push-off shortens the stride, slows you down and prevents the backs of your thighs and calves from getting the proper amount of exercise.

Your *arm swing* will assist your legs by counterbalancing the torque on the torso. Your leg and hip move backward on one side while your arm and shoulder move backward on the other side. Your elbows will be flexed to about a 90-degree angle. Your hands will face inward with a *loose fist* position. On the forward swing, the hand will move somewhat across the chest with the hand stopping at midchest level, just below the nipple line. The backward-swinging arm will stop when the hand is about at the back of the hip (see photo on next page). You will want your elbows to stay close to your body. An elbow that wanders too wide reduces efficiency by excessively turning your shoulders, causing you to use more energy.

Compared to running, walking does not create a great deal of stress on the foot. Running can create an amount of stress that is several times the weight of the body. However, even the lesser amount of shock created when your heel strikes the pavement is found to move through the legs, back, neck and to the head.[2]

When you begin walking, have an instructor, if you are in a class, or a friend check your posture. When viewed from the side, is your torso upright? Do you have a slight whole body lean from the ankles? The arms should swing naturally. When walking slowly they will be relaxed. As speed picks up, the elbows will flex to about 90 degrees.

When viewed from the front, are your feet excessively turned in or out? Is your foot placement such that lines drawn on the inside of each foot would be about three inches apart?

Your elbows should be flexed to about a 90-degree angle.

Think of yourself walking along a three-inch-wide line, such as a tennis court boundary. Does the push off seem to be from the big toe?

Your breathing will be natural. Many like to breathe in through the nose for one or two steps, then exhale through the mouth for one or two steps. If you begin to tire, try exhaling harder. This will allow you to breathe in more deeply on the next breath.

Walking form is important to us so that we don't bring on self-injury. To train properly, form is important. When a body in motion begins to fatigue, good form might turn into poor form. When this happens, perhaps it's time to slow down or even stop and call it a day.

FITNESS WALKING

As with any other aerobic activity, you should exercise at 65 percent to 90 percent of your maximum heart rate to have the greatest effect. (See Chapter 5.) You will need to measure your heart rate with a pulse monitor or by taking your pulse for six seconds and multiplying by 10. Soon, you will have a pretty good idea of how fast you need to walk in order to be at your target range.

You will want to get an idea of how fast you are walking. This is called your *pace*. Go to a school track. Most tracks are one-quarter mile in length. The track is a great place to work on pace. How long does it take you to walk a half-mile or a mile at a good pace for you? You can chart your mileage and times. Then, when you go for a long walk, you will have an idea of what pace you are going and how far you went.

If it takes you four minutes to do a quarter-mile, you know you're on a pace to walk a mile in 16 minutes. So, if you get a pretty good understanding of pace, you can go out on a walk for 32 minutes, turn around and return to your starting point and log in four miles. It's that simple.

HAVING FUN

Have fun when you are fitness walking. Walk in interesting places — along the beach, in the woods or through the parks. Enjoy nature or the people you see. It is not advised to use earphones. You will want to hear traffic or any warnings or greetings coming your way. You have probably already walked and talked at some time in your life. Why not do your exercise walking and talking with a friend? You can catch up on the day's events, do some planning or solve the world's problems.

While most of your walking will probably be "right foot, left foot," variations in your foot and arm movement help you to exercise different muscles. With so many different body types and so many different goals and objectives, there might well be different ways to walk for what you need.

Walking backward is a way to alter your walking workout. Perhaps you are a bit fatigued and feel that you are slumping forward or perhaps your back hurts a little. Walk backward for a few hundred yards. This will allow you to change muscle groups and put your skeletal system back in alignment. Walking backward is a super training exercise. It elevates the heart rate and stretches the Achilles' tendons, calves, hamstrings, hip flexors, back muscles and the shoulder and neck. When was

Carioca

the last time you went backward to get ahead in life? Practice does make a big difference and walking backward can make a positive difference in your fitness program.

To exercise the muscles at the sides of the hips and on the inside of the hips, you can do the *carioca* (see photos on previous page). This action, which is used as a hip warm up by many athletes, is done by turning sideways to the direction of your walk. If you are moving to your left, your right leg will cross in front of your left leg on one step, then your left leg will take its step, then your right leg will cross behind your left leg, then the left leg will take another step. Your feet will point at nearly right angles to the direction you are traveling. After 50 yards or so, turn your body 180-degrees and move to your right on your walking path. Now, your left leg will cross in front of the right leg, then in back of it.

You can also add some arm action to your walking.

- Exaggerate your arm swing, bringing your arms farther up and farther back on each step. This will increase the exercise for the muscles in the front of your shoulders and top of your chest during the forward swing, then the muscles at the back of your shoulders and upper back on your backward swing (see photo below).

- Raise your arms sideways, as if you were doing jumping jacks. This will exercise the muscles at the top of your shoulders.

- Flex your elbow by touching your hand to your shoulder on each swing to give your biceps a bit of exercise.

- Pretend you are boxing or punching a bag. This will give your triceps (the back of the upper arms) and top of the shoulders some extra work. Or you can punch up into the air (see photo below).

Exaggerated arm swings   *Punching an imaginary bag*

- Spread your arms wide at shoulder level and alternately touch your upper chest. This will work the tops of the shoulders, the biceps and the triceps.

Walking in the hills not only changes the scenery but also gives you more exercise in the muscles that move the ankle and foot in and out (pronation and eversion). It is also good for most lower-back problems because it strengthens the lower-back muscles, especially when the terrain forces you to walk with one foot higher than the other, such as when walking along a slope.

Walking backwards

Depending on how high your pulse has risen, you might need to cool down. If you are monitoring your pulse, you can slow down your exercise until your pulse is about 100 to 105 beats per minute or lower. This is more easily done if you have a heart monitor (a chest strap that transfers your heart rate to a wristwatch type of device.) If you are not very flexible, the end of the workout is the best time to stretch. Your warm muscles and connective tissues will better adapt to the stretch and are more likely to allow the stretched connective tissue to remain stretched. It is wise to stretch the Achilles' tendons and calf muscles, the hip flexors and extensors and the lower back.

You might also want to do some strength work for some of your muscles. See the Chapter 19 on strength training for exercises for your abdominal muscles, lower back, hip flexors and extensors, calves, ankles and any other areas that you would like to strengthen.

You should walk 30 to 60 minutes each day, but whatever amount you do will help. If it is only 20 minutes every other day, you will still have more than an hour of exercise each week that you otherwise would not have had. Remember, for fitness, walk fast; for fat reduction, walk long. For fitness, you will want to get your pulse to the level discussed in the last chapter your target rate for your fitness walk for 30 minutes. For fat reduction, you can be at 50 percent to 65 percent of that level for one to two hours.

BIOMECHANICS OF RACEWALKING

If you are walking in competition, you must not only have at least one foot in contact with the ground at all times, you must straighten the leg that has contact with the ground, if only for an instant. This requirement is what gives racewalkers that active hip movement. Judges at racewalking competitions must be trained to see that both of these requirements are completed with every step. (Some of the leaders in the women's walking competition were disqualified near the end of the race in the Sydney Olympics in 2000.)

You will have a slight forward lean from your ankles, not a forward bend from the hip. About five degrees is right for most people. This will allow for a more effective pushoff.

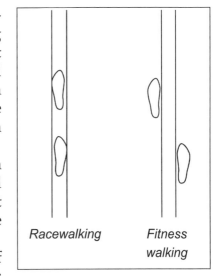

*Racewalking   Fitness
                        walking*

While fitness walking, the insides of your feet follow a path about three inches apart, as if you were walking over but not touching a three inch line. In racewalking, you will walk directly on the line. Your feet will follow each other.

At the heel strike, your ankle will have about a 90-degree angle to your shinbone. This helps to straighten your leg as the race rules require. The force of the impact will begin at the outer part of your heel,

	Starting Speed (miles covered/ pace of miles per hour)	Increase speed by .5 mph	% of max heart rate
Level 1	1/3	after 6 weeks Again after 15 wks	60
Level 2	1.5/3	Again after 15 wks	60-70
Level 3	2/3	After 6 weeks Again after 11 wks	70
Level 4	2.5/3.5	After 7 weeks Again after 11 wks.	70
Level 5	3/4	After 4 weeks	70
(Plan on exercising at 80% of your maximum heart rate within 6 weeks if you are in Level 5; within 5 months if you are in Level 1.)			

then roll inward until at the push off it is in about the middle of the ball of the foot and toes. The push off, then, will be from the middle of the front of the foot. The rules require that your push-off foot must still be in contact with the ground until the landing foot strikes the ground.

Your arms will be flexed at the elbow at 90 degrees. They will swing nearly straight forward and back, not around. But since the hips are rotating with each step, your shoulders will rotate to compensate. This will force your forearms slightly across your chest. So, your hand, when swinging forward, will come slightly across your chest but never as far as the middle of your chest. It will come about as high as the armpit. The arm swinging backward will stop when the hand is at a level of about the top of the hip.

The major differences between racewalking and running are that in running, the support leg will not straighten completely, while in racewalking, it must. Also, in running there will be a time when both feet are off the ground; in racewalking, one foot must always be on the ground.

Racewalking is not for beginners, but if you get into good shape and want more exercise, it is an option. And, of course, if you want to enter into walking competitions, such as the Olympics, you must race-walk.

BEGINNING YOUR WALKING PROGRAM

Start slowly. If you are not in good condition, you will want to avoid the muscle soreness that results when starting to exercise. So, depending on your condition, start with just 12 to 15 minutes of slow walking. It is best to exercise daily, but since your conditioning will last about two days before you lose it, you can rest a day, then add about two to five minutes to your first walk. Each time you walk, add about two to five minutes to your last walking period. After several days, you should be up to a half hour of walking.

If you are walking for fitness, you can begin walking faster for your half-hour walks. If your purpose is losing weight, keep adding five minutes each walk until you reach at least an hour of walking. For weight loss, the time spent is more important than the speed. For fitness, the speed becomes more important. Therefore, for fat reduction, you can profit from two hours or more of exercise. (Body fat is used for fuel more efficiently during longer exercise

Walking for fun and fitness

CHECKLIST FOR RACEWALKING FORM

☐ Is your support leg straight early in the stride or under your hip?

☐ Are your feet landing on the same line, directly under the middle of your hips?

☐ Is your arm action correct? (Back hand no higher than the top of the hips forward hand not crossing the midline of the chest and no higher than the armpit.)

CHECKLIST FOR CALORIES USED PER MINUTE WHEN WALKING AT DIFFERENT SPEEDS FOR VARYING BODY WEIGHTS

Speed in MPH	Calories used for person weighing				
	100 lbs.	125 lbs.	150 lbs.	175 lbs.	200 lbs.
2	1.86	2.3	2.8	3.3	3.7
3	2.5	3.1	3.7	4.3	4.9
4	3.7	6.4	5.6	6.6	7.4
5	6	7.5	9	10.5	12

CHECKLIST FOR FITNESS WALKING FORM

☐ Is your torso upright?

☐ Do you have a slight whole body lean from the ankles?

☐ Are your feet pointed straight ahead?

☐ Is your foot placement such that lines drawn on the inside of each foot would be about three inches apart?

☐ Do the arms swing naturally?

---

periods.) For fitness, you are more interested in making your heart work harder, so a half-hour to an hour of fast walking with your heart rate in the target range will be effective.

While you do not need a set workout program to begin your walking exercise, because every person is somewhat different in terms of physical conditioning and motivation, here are a few guidelines:

1. FREQUENCY PER WEEK: Plan on walking at least five days each week. Walk two days, rest one; then walk three days, rest one.

2. WARM UP: Walk slowly, then pick up the pace for three to five minutes.

3. MILEAGE PER DAY: If you are in poor condition, start with just one mile of walking per day. If you are in excellent shape, you can

---

AMERICAN HEART ASSOCIATION'S RECOMMENDATIONS FOR SLOWLY EASING INTO AN EFFECTIVE WALKING PROGRAM
☐ Week One: warm up for five minutes, exercise for five minutes, cool down for five minutes.
☐ Weeks Two through Six: add two minutes of exercise to the previous week's workout. For example, during week two, one would warm up for five minutes, exercise for seven minutes and cool down for five minutes.
☐ Week Seven: add three minutes each week to the previous week's workout. For example, during week seven, one would exercise for 18 minutes, etc.
☐ From week thirteen on, each individual works at her own individual heart rate (see Chapter Five) for 40 or more minutes.

begin with a three-mile walk. (If you have done the fitness evaluation test in Chapter 5, you can use the guidelines below that are based on the Rockport Walking Program.)

4.   COOL DOWN: Two to five minutes

WARM UP AND COOL DOWN

Hard exercise requires a warm up to get the blood circulating to the muscles and to get the muscles contracting effectively. For walking, the mere movement of slow walking progressing to faster walking should be enough. If you like to stretch your calves or hamstrings, wait until you have walked a few minutes. While we have long heard that stretching is an essential part of a warm up, recent research does not indicate that this is always true (see Chapter 4). But if you feel like stretching, stretch. Just do it slowly.

CONCERNING THE TEMPERATURE

You can walk in just about any temperature. If it is warm, it is best to exercise before the heat of the day. Drink plenty of water before and during your walk. If it is raining, you can put on your rain clothes and enjoy the weather. If it is cold, just bundle up, but you still need your water. If it is snowing you can walk or cross-country ski. If you live near a mall, you can take advantage of the all-year comfort and walk inside. Of course, you can also walk in school buildings or in the protected walkways.

Walking when it is cold will not give you a cold. Cold air, however, cannot hold as much moisture as warm air. This dryness can reduce the mucous lining in your nose and increase the chance that any viruses you are already carrying can enter your blood stream and give you an upper respiratory infection — a *cold*. This can happen indoors or out. In fact, the chances are higher indoors because people with viruses in their noses are closer!

Notes

1. Light, L.H. et al. "Skeletal transients on heel strike in normal walking with different footwear." *Journal of Biomechanics* 13 (1980): 477-480.)
2. Voloshin, A.S. and J. Wosk, J. "An in vivo study of low back pain and shock absorption in the human locomotor system." *Journal of Biomechanics.* 15 (1982): 21-27

7

THE BIOMECHANICS OF DISTANCE RUNNING

Some runners find contentment and enjoyment in simply running for fitness. Others, however, are seriously interested in understanding more completely and comprehending the smaller details of how the body can run more effectively. This chapter is for these people.

Running speed, from long-distance running to sprinting, depends on the length of the stride and the number of strides per minute (stride frequency). In sprinting, the strides are long and the frequency is fast. If that pace could be maintained, a runner could cover a mile in about two minutes and 40 seconds, covering 10 or more yards per second. But in a marathon, the miles are covered in five to six minutes. Consequently, marathoners' strides are shorter and their frequency is slower. Distance runners, depending on the distance, will generally cover only 2.5 to six meters per second. (Studies indicate that the change from normal walking — not racewalking — to running occurs when the person is moving at about 2.5 meters per second.)

The potential to be a sprinter or a long-distance runner depends to a large degree on heredity. If you are muscular with a large number of fast-twitch muscle fibers, you have the potential to be a sprinter. If you are slim with a large number of slow-twitch muscles, which give you muscular endurance, you are better equipped to run distances. Depending on your training, you can create more of either type of muscle fibers. You can also increase your abilities in either type of running by using the proper biomechanics.

BIOMECHANICS FOR DISTANCE RUNNERS

The mechanics of the body (bio) help us to analyze every movement from standing or walking to running or hitting a golf ball. In analyzing running, several methods have been used. The joints might be marked so that they trace a path on a film or a computer-generated program. Force plates (flat-pressure measuring devices that are put on floors or tracks) measure the forces generated by the step in landing and taking off. Pres-

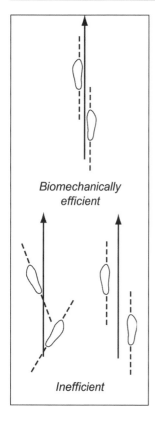

Biomechanically
efficient

Inefficient

sure sensors might be used in the shoes to determine exactly where and when the forces of the foot plant are generated. (Such information is used in designing running shoes.) Scientists generally measure the actions and forces when a runner is running about four to five yards per second.

The foot should hit the ground just about under the hips. A runner should not reach out to increase the stride because it will negatively affect this important criterion of effective running. The angle at the thigh to a vertical line drawn down from the hips is about 25 degrees. The knee will still be slightly flexed when the foot hits the ground. There will be a 10- to 20-degree angle at the knee. Even at the end of the stride, just before the push off, the knee will still be flexed 10 to 15 degrees. When the foot hits the ground, the angle of the ankle will be just about what it is when standing — 90 degrees. Depending on the amount of flexion at the knee the angle can be greater. Then, as the foot moves behind the hips, we expect an additional 20 degrees or so of plantar flexion (movement of the shin toward the toes).

The foot on landing tends to pronate (the middle of the foot moving toward the ground). This is a consequence of the landing force, and the fact that the leg is angled in at one or two degrees puts additional strain on the foot to flatten. To ease one's balance it is easy to see that when running, the landing of the feet should be close to the midline of the body. (Studies have indicated that the inside of the shoe stays close to the body's midline, varying from 1.5 inches from the midline to a half-inch past it.) As the runner speeds up, foot placement becomes a bit wider than it does when running slowly.

Since the normal standing position has the feet several inches out from the midline, we can see why the leg must angle in to assist in maintaining balance. The inward angle of the legs forces the feet to pronate on landing so that the foot can flatten effectively. This happens to a lesser degree if you are running barefoot. Shoes actually increase the pronation and cause possibly harmful stresses to the ligaments and tendons in the feet. As the runner becomes fatigued, the amount of pronation is also increased.[1]

As the knee leads the foot in the recovery, the angle of flexion at the knee is about 70 degrees. The angle of the thigh is about 31 degrees.

(Some studies have found it to be between 26 and 35 degrees.) The tibia, the bone in the lower leg, tends to rotate inward one or two degrees. This may increase the chances of knee stress and injury. The more a runner's ankles and feet pronate, the greater the twist of the tibia.

The arm action decreases as the speed decreases. In distance running, the arms should be relaxed and held low. Holding them low means that the shoulders will be relaxed. If the muscles of the neck and those connecting the shoulders to the spine are tense, you would be using extra energy to do this, and you would probably become very tense in the shoulder area. The hands should be slightly cupped or carried with a loose fist. Running with the hands tightly clenched or totally open will increase the tension in the forearm. This is not only uncomfortable but also uses energy that could be used instead for leg power.

It would appear to make sense to have the elbows moving directly forward and back. But since the torso will twist somewhat — more at faster speeds — a straight forward and back arm movement would not be natural because the arms must work in a plane according to where the shoulders are pointing.

The arms can aid the body.

The action of the arms does not propel the body forward; the legs do this. The arms can aid in lifting the body somewhat, which will increase the stride length just a little. They also aid in counteracting the twist of the torso, which is caused by the thigh moving forward, then backward in the stride cycle. They do this more effectively if the hands cross a little in front of the chest.

The biomechanics of running will change in the same person depending on the speed of running.[2] It was found that the backward extension of the hip increased only about three degrees when running faster, but the forward flexing of the hip (the hip-thigh angle) increased by more than 22 degrees. It had always been thought that our hips would extend much farther back when running faster. Other studies have confirmed the findings but have given values as much as a five-degree increase of hip extension at the push off and as much as a 25-degree hip flexion in the follow-through action.[3]

The angle of the knee while moving forward will also change with increasing speed from less than 90 degrees when running slowly (four meters per second) to more than 110 degrees at a fast pace (seven meters per second). But the angle of the knee while the foot is on the ground changes only a few degrees, being straighter at higher speeds. The angle of the foot at the foot strike changes very little.

Stride length is a factor in developing speed but it might not be as important for distance runners. In fact, elite-level runners might not take as long a stride as good runners do.[4] This shorter stride length reduces energy consumption and the braking effect that occurs when the foot hits the ground. This braking effect is increased if the runner's foot lands in advance of the front of the hips.

Studies indicate that when a stride is either too long or too short, it increases the amount of energy used. Most runners will have a natural stride that will be most efficient. That stride will increase as the speed increases.

The angle of the foot at the foot strike changes very little.

MUSCLE ACTIVITY

Muscles contract when they receive an electrical impulse. That impulse can come from your conscious thought (I want to contract this muscle), from a repeated habit, a learned coordination, such as when running, or from a reflex action. When running slowly your coordination will take over. You don't have to think "right leg, left leg." But if you wanted to run faster, you might have to concentrate harder on contracting a muscle. Understanding how, when and why your muscles contract will allow you to develop a strength-training program for your running, if you are so inclined.

A stretched muscle is more likely to begin to contract. Perhaps you have been in a doctor's office sitting on a table and the doctor hits your patellar tendon, just below your kneecap, and your leg kicks out — or at least it should. The fact that there was tension in your quadriceps muscle (the front of the thigh) which was quickly increased by the hammer striking the tendon that attaches that muscle to the bone just below your knee, made your muscles contract. This is called the stretch reflex. It is often a factor in the contraction of your muscles while running.

Another property of the stretched muscle if it is absorbing a force, such as when landing from a jump or a running stride, is that more muscle fibers are contracting when absorbing the force, and they will be able to be used for jumping or striding if you immediately use them. This is called the stretch-shortening cycle. The higher the force, from the jump or stride, the greater the potential for contracting that muscle, with a resulting increase of power will be.

Plyometric exercises for increasing running stride or jumping ability use this ability. If you were to jump down from a box and immediately jump up, or if you were to take long bounding strides, you would be making use of this stretch-shortening cycle.

The *gluteus maximus* muscle begins to contract at the end of the recovery phase, when your thigh is coming forward, and continues for about the first third of the backward movement of your thigh. This is necessary to allow your leg to slow down so that it can begin its backward power thrust. The contraction is at least partially caused by the fact that it is being stretched.

The *hip abductors* (muscles that move the thighs away from the body) contract at about the same time as the gluteus maximus — the end of the recovery and the beginning of the power phase. Their contraction helps to stabilize the hips on landing.

The *hip adductors* (the muscles that bring the thighs toward the middle of the body) contract through the entire cycle of the recovery and power phase. Without their contractions, your legs would move outside of the midline of the body. Their contractions, therefore, hold the thighs in so that the feet can hit close to the midline of the body and keep you balanced.

The hamstrings (the muscles in the back of the thighs that pull the thighs backward and flex the knee) work during the last 25 to 40 percent of the forward leg swing. At the beginning of the leg swing, the knee seems to flex without the aid of these muscles. It seems to be the speed of swinging the thigh forward that brings the lower part of the leg upward. Near the end of the leg swing, the hamstrings seem to contract to slow down the thigh, as does the gluteus maximus, and to control the straightening of the leg. Investigators are not in agreement as to whether the hamstrings contract only during the first half of the power action of bringing the thigh back or whether they act through the whole power cycle.

The *quadriceps* (four muscles in the front of the thighs — three of which bring the thigh forward while all four straighten the knee) work during the last half of the swing phase and during the first half of the backward power stroke. They bring the knee to an almost extended position. They also absorb some of the shock of the landing. After the thighs pass under the hips, they show little muscular activity. However, one study indicates that with greater speed, this muscle works much harder, drawing the conclusions of the researcher that it is a primary muscle in running. [5]

The *tibialis anterior* (the muscle in the front of the shin bone) holds the foot up during the swing of the recovery and while the heel is hitting the ground—the heel strike. It continues to work while the foot is on the ground. A recent study showed that its rate of contraction was very high for a much longer time than had been believed. This may be a factor contributing to *shin splints*, a common running ailment. [6]

The *gastrocnemius* and the *soleus* (the muscles in the back of the leg or the calf) are active for slower runners during the last part of the swing phase and through 50 to 80 percent of the stance phase, when the foot is on the ground. For a person running on the toes, these muscles are more active prior to the foot plant as it extends the ankle, allowing the toes or the ball of the foot to land first. People sprinting or running on their toes will have these muscles active throughout the time the foot is on the ground and throughout the push off phase, where they are very important in the final part of the push off.

GROUND REACTION FORCES

The ground reaction force refers to the amount of force your foot is exerting against the ground. It includes the amount of force you transmit when landing and the amount of force you exert when pushing off. Obviously, the more force you can exert while pushing off, the greater will be your stride length. It refers to the idea of Sir Isaac Newton in his third law of motion — that every action has an equal and opposite reaction. In running it is a combination of your body weight, whether or not your hips are moving up and down, and the speed at which you are running. Running downhill will also increase these forces by more than double.[7] Running barefoot also increases the forces because there is no cushioning effect as there is with most shoes.

The faster you run, the shorter the period of time that your foot is on the ground, so all of the forces must be absorbed more quickly. This can be a factor in injury. This is because the shock of the landing must be absorbed through the bones of the foot and ankle, the leg, the knee, the thigh, the hips and the lower back. Each of these body parts is therefore subject to *overuse injuries* because of the continual recurring of the stresses. The bones, ligaments, tendons and muscles might not be sufficiently strong to continue to work injury free. When you realize that when running a mile each foot will strike the ground 450 to 600 times you can understand the fact that overuse injuries can occur.

ENVIRONMENTAL FACTORS AFFECTING RUNNING

Overcoming the resistance to the air is a significant factor in running. Obviously, the larger the runner, the greater the air resistance. Also, the more head wind, the more energy that must be used to overcome it. Even with no wind there is a significant amount of energy that must be used to overcome it. It has been calculated that a middle-distance runner (800 to 1600 meters) running at close to a world-record pace increases the amount of energy used to overcome the air resistance by seven to eight percent. Sprinters increase their energy expenditure by 13 to 16 percent, even with no wind.

Running into the wind is, of course, more difficult, and running with the wind is easier. But running with the wind behind you reduces your energy output only half of that which would be needed if you were running into the same wind. So, if running into the wind requires you to use an additional 300 calories, running with that same wind at your back would save you only 150 calories, not the 300 that you might think you saved. So, if you were running around a track with a wind blowing, you will need more energy than if you were running the same speed around the same track with no wind. In fact, it has been calculated that your time would be reduced about .3 seconds per lap on a quarter-mile track with a five mph wind.

Your shoes, in addition to being potential injury preventers, can make a difference in your speed. Obviously, a lighter shoe will use less energy to move. Even one-third of an ounce (75 grams) can make a difference.[8]

CHECKLIST FOR RUNNING EFFECTIVELY
☐ Head up
☐ Torso up
☐ Body lean should be from the ankles to the shoulders, not the hips to the shoulders.
☐ The landing foot should be just about under the hips to avoid a braking action.
☐ The hands should not cross the midline of the body during their forward swing.

The amount of energy used increases 1.2 percent for each 100 grams (4.5 ounces). Also, if you run with orthotics in your shoes to correct your stride or reduce your injuries, you must also consider the weight of the orthotic in reducing your running efficiency.

If your shoes have effective cushioning, you might reduce your energy costs by up to three percent. Here, we wonder if the increased weight of the cushioning is offset by the added weight. It might be six of one and a half a dozen of the other!

RUNNING EFFICIENCY

Becoming more efficient either in your mechanics of running or your aerobic conditioning (heart-blood-lungs-muscles) makes you faster and enables you to run farther. If a world-record holder were to improve only two percent, her 10K time would drop 32 seconds and the marathon time would drop two minutes. Such an improvement can come from equipment, such as the shoes, or from developing a more efficient stride, but most will come from the aerobic conditioning of the heart, lungs, blood and muscles.

A number of other factors will affect your running efficiency. Having wider hips, as many women do, will change the angle of the thigh when the feet are placed near the midline of the body when running. Increased body fat is also a factor. (The average woman has eight to 10 percent more body fat than the average man.) It requires more energy to move the extra weight. Of course, there is a large overlap between all women and all men. Many men have wider hips than many women, and many men have more body fat than many women. These two factors seem to be responsible for some of the increased injuries that women runners incur. But we should observe that the average female distance runner has about the same amount of fat as the average nonrunning man.

Notes

1. McClay, I., and K. Manal. "Coupling parameters in runners with normal and excessive pronation." *Journal of Applied Biomechanics*, 13:1 (1997): 109-124 and VanGheluwe, B. and Madsen, C. "Frontal rearfoot kinematics in running prior to volitional exhaustion." *Journal of Applied Biomechanics* 13:1 (1997): 67-75 .

2. Sinning, W.E. and H.L. Forsyth "Lower limb actions while running at different velocities." *Medicine and Science in Sports and Exercise.* 2 (1970): 28-34.

3. Nilsson, T. and J. Halbertsma. "Changes in leg movements and muscle activity with speed of locomotion and mode of progression in humans." *Acta Physiologica Scandinavica.* 123:4 (1985) 457-475.

4. Cavanagh, P.R. et al."A biomechanical comparison of elite and good distance runners," In P. Milvy (ed) *The Marathon: Physiological, Medical, Epidemiological, and Psychological Studies.* New York: New York Academy of Sciences. (1977): 328-345.

5. Montgomery, W. et al. "Electromyographic analysis of hip and knee musculature during running." *American Journal of sports Medicine.* 22:2 (1994): 272-278.

6. Reber, L., et al. "Muscular control of the ankle in running" *American Journal of Sports Medicine.* 21:6 (1993): 805-810.

7. Buczek, F. and Cavanagh, P. "Stance phase knee and ankle kinematics and kinetics during level and downhill running." *Medicine and Science in Sport and Exercise.* 22:5 (1990): 669-677.

8. Frederick, E.C. et al. "The effect of shoe weight on aerobic demands of running." In L. Prukop (ed) *Proceedings of the World Congress on Sports Medicine. Vienna: World Congress on Sports Medicine.* (1984): 616-625.

8

JOGGING, DISTANCE RUNNING AND MARATHONS

Many women start as walkers or joggers. As they progress, they want to move farther or faster. Often, the desire for competition or an urge to test themselves emerges, and what was once a fitness walker or jogger becomes a competitor looking for five and 10K runs and perhaps marathons.

Marathons and racing have been mentioned to give you an idea of some of the possibilities available to you. In Chapter 10, we will introduce orienteering, which is another popular activity for runners in which map reading skills become as important, or more important, than the running. Find what you like to do — jogging or running, exercising alone or with others, with or without competition, with music or in silence, on the beach or in the woods. The point is to enjoy yourself in a manner suited to you while your body gets the exercise it needs to feel good today and to help you live longer.

JOGGING

Jogging is slow running, usually landing on the heels. Well-conditioned male joggers will cover a mile in about a seven to nine minutes (4:21 to 5:36 per kilometer), while women will cover the same distance in about eight to 10 minutes (4:58 to 6:13 per kilometer). Of course, there is a wide variation in speeds for both sexes. Nearly all runners will jog during some part of their workouts. Some, of course, only jog. The amount of jogging you do depends on your physical condition and your exercise objectives. If physical conditioning is your only concern, you can merely jog, but make certain that your heart rate reaches the levels needed for an effective workout (see Chapter 5).

Joggers are generally more interested in being fit, reducing body fat and cutting their risk for heart disease. Runners might have the same motivations but are usually interested in getting there faster. There is more interest in competition.

General fitness requires only three or four days a week of exercising at 60 to 85 percent of your target heart rate for 30 minutes. But so many

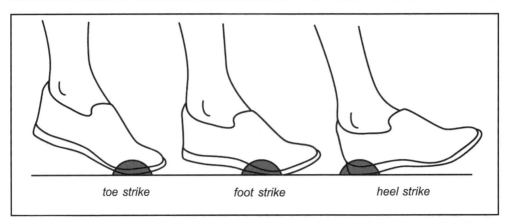

Foot landing possibilities: Faster runners tend to land on the balls of their feet and their toes (called a toe strike). Somewhat slower runners will often land on the area from the ball of the foot and slightly behind it (called a foot strike). Joggers are more likely to land on their heels (a heel strike).

people find jogging or running refreshing, they do it daily. And although Dr. Ken Cooper has said that most of the benefits for your heart are accomplished during the first 30 minutes of exercise and nearly all benefits are accomplished within an hour, many people enjoy longer jogging periods.

DEVELOPING YOUR PACE

In any distance greater than a 200-meter sprint, you should know how fast you are going. This is particularly true if you are going to race, and its importance increases with the length of the race. In racing, you

Good running technique for long distance

should set a goal as to how fast you want to run your 10K or marathon then break that speed down into 400-meter and mile increments. For example, if you wanted to run a 2:10 marathon, an Olympic-level pace, you would need to average a 4:50 mile. If you aspire to a 2:36 marathon, then a six-minute mile will do. A recreational runner would quite possibly be happy with a 4:20 marathon — a 9:40-per-mile pace.

Middle distance runners

MUSCLE FATIGUE

Running a long distance increases the fatigue in the muscles. Even well-conditioned marathoners find fatigue factors setting in after running 20 miles. In order to keep the same pace, the runner must work harder, particularly forcing the quadriceps (front of the thigh) and gastrocmenius (back of calf) to contract more forcefully. It can take two to three times as much effort to keep the same speed. Part of the reason is that when the muscle is stretched (eccentric contraction) when fatigued, it does not have the same elasticity, so it cannot store the energy then deliver it again with the shortening (concentric) contraction.[1]

Running style changes when running the marathon or finishing a triathlon (which, depending on the distance, finishes with a run from five km to a full marathon). Fatigue often forces us to change our running biomechanics with a resultant loss of efficiency and an increased energy cost. The types of biomechanical changes are somewhat different for each runner and also seem to be dependent on the event being run. For example, a triathlete who has already finished the swimming and cycling segments and is beginning the running portion of the event tends to lean further forward than would be done if the same athlete were running a marathon without previously swimming and cycling. Additionally, the stride length is reduced and there is a greater angle at the knee during the recovery period for the triathlete.[2] While these findings probably are largely related to the increased fatigue of the triathlon, they do indicate that fatigue can, and probably will, make us alter our biomechanics. Therefore, it is wise to concentrate on our running form as we become tired.

ORGANIZED RECREATIONAL RUNNING AND COMPETITION

Joining a running club can help you increase your circle of fitness-interested friends. You can generally find a local club in the phone book or by asking at a shop that sells running shoes. Here you can find people with similar interests and abilities who might want to run with you.

As you improve in your conditioning you might want to test yourself in a race situation. 5K (five kilometers — about three miles) and 10K runs are held often in most parts of the country. Your local shoe store, running club or the Internet can inform you of where and when these will occur. These are also good places to meet new people.

These events are usually organized according to age groups with winners in each group. If you are not competitive, don't worry about winning. Just enjoy the experience. If you decide that you want to compete, a five or 10K run will give you an idea of the times to shoot for in your age group.

THE MARATHON

As was earlier noted, the idea for the marathon race began with the run of the Greek soldier Pheidippides from Marathon to Athens in 490 B.C. to announce the victory over the Persians. When the modern Olympic games began in Athens in 1896, the same run became part of the event, and the Greeks placed eight runners in the top nine finishers. Another Greek, Dimitrou Yordanides, has the honor of being the oldest runner to ever complete a marathon. He finished the 1976 race, when he was 98 years old, in seven hours and 33 minutes. So, we definitely have the Greeks to thank for our quest for gold and glory by running a marathon. For many fitness runners, merely completing the marathon run is reward enough. But you don't have to compete to have fun in running or jogging or to gain the fitness benefits from these activities.

In the event that you might be interested in the progress of women

Women's run in Sweden; more than 30,000 women participated.

Caloric Expenditure per minute for running at various speeds for various body weights.					
Speed	100 lb. person	125 lb.	150 lb.	175 lb.	200 lb.
5.5 mph (11 minutes per mile)	7.1	9.0	10.7	12.5	14.3
7 mph (8.5 minutes per mile)	9.3	11.7	14	16.3	18.5
9 mph (7 minutes per mile)	11.2	13.9	15.5	18.5	20.7
12 mph (5 minutes per mile)	13.1	16.4	19.6	22.6	26.2
Sprinting	15.3	19.2	23	26.9	30.7

during the last century — Baron de Coubertain, the founder of the modern Olympics, didn't think that women should compete in any event. In protest, a Greek woman named Melpomene ran in the marathon in the first of the modern Olympics in Athens in 1896.

In 1966, Roberta Gibb ran the Boston Marathon as an unofficial entrant. Her time was a respectable 3:20. The next year, Kathrine Switzer, a student at Syracuse University, officially entered as K.V. Switzer — but it wasn't until part way through the race that K.V. was recognized to be a female. In spite of the fact that she was wearing her official number an official physically tried to eject her from the race. Kathrine's boyfriend, Tom Miller — a nationally ranked hammer thrower, shoulder blocked the official away. Kathrine not only finished the race but campaigned for the inclusion of women in the race. In 1972, women were finally allowed to run "The Marathon." Only two women ran faster than three hours in the race. By 1994, 30 women ran under 2:30.

Grete Weitz, the nine-time winner of the New York Marathon and Olympic silver medalis,t began a "run" in Olso only for women. A many as 42,000 have competed. Girls and women of every age have joined. Some run to compete. Most walk and run for the exercise and because it is a women's "happening." While the first flight to start are the highly competitive women, the great majority of participants are there for some fitness and lots of fun. Groups of women walk and run together, often singing. Some dress in costumes. Witches and princesses, cats and clowns all running and walking. While most started training weeks before the event, and the 5K distance helps in one's fitness — whether walking or running — the mental side of the event is often foremost in the women's minds. Friends, neighbors and business associates train together, walk and run together, then party together afterwards. Several other countries have copied Grete's formula for aiding in women's health and fitness.

Running the marathon is the ultimate test for many who want to run. Certainly, preparing for a marathon by running many miles each week will increase your fitness level, so there are many positives. Also, since marathons are run in nearly every corner of the world, there is an opportunity to travel.

While the positive effects of training our bodies are well-known, there are some short-term negatives. Training, if less than 10 miles per day, increases the immune system's potential to help us avoid infections and illnesses, including many cancers, but it is severely reduced for a few days after running a marathon. A recent study of Los Angeles Marathon registrants and participants compared those who had registered to run — but did not — to those who ran and finished. Among those who ran, 14 percent soon developed upper-respiratory infections (colds). Among those who did not run, only two percent developed colds in the same period.[3] There seems to be an increase in infections in people running more than 60 miles (90 km) per week.

The primary muscle fuel, glycogen, reduces by about 80 percent immediately after a marathon, despite a high carbohydrate diet, but returns to normal in about a week.[4] While the reduction is more than some might have expected, the fact that it soon returns to normal relieves our concerns. Just don't run another marathon in heavy competition within a week of completing one! Of course, people nearly always wait several weeks between marathon competitions.

The types of leg and foot problems that occur during the running of a marathon are many: corns, cramps, calluses, blisters, plantar fasciitis and other problems in the knees, ankles and feet. The constantly repeated stress of each landing and each takeoff is increased by the landing on the hard street surface and by running at a faster than normal pace because of the competition. However, the number of injuries is less for those who are well-trained. The more miles you have run in preparation for the race and in your total training history, the less chance you have of developing a problem during a marathon.[5]

ULTRAMARATHONS

Ultramarathons are a challenge that some people enjoy. An example would be the 110-kilometer race — more than twice the marathon distance of 42 km. It has recently been postulated that women can outrun men at the longer distances. Studies show that up to the distance of a marathon, the men are more efficient. At about 66 kilometers, many women and men are about equal. After that, the women have superior resistance to fatigue.[6] Not all research indicates this same phenomenon. The problem is whether you take equally trained men and women, as was done in the above study, or whether you take men and women who run similar marathon times. When the latter is done, the women were already relatively better runners so the results might be different.

In one study of ultramarathoners, several hormones and other body chemicals were analyzed before the race, after running 33 km, after 75 km and at the end of the race. These were compared to a control group that followed the race. It was found that *cortisol*, which can have an anti-inflammatory effect, and beta-endorphins, which tend to reduce depression and give the "exercise high," both increased during the race. The female *luteinizing hormone* was lower at the end of the race than at the beginning. Most of these changes occurred during the first third of the race. But the male hormone *testosterone* continued to drop throughout the race.[7]

WHAT IS REALISTIC FOR YOU?

What goals do you have to enjoy your increased fitness? Certainly, you don't have to compete. Do you prefer to be alone with your thoughts while you run? Do you want companionship? Do you want to compete? Each of these is a worthwhile goal. Each is easily possible. Do you want fitness and solitude, fitness with friendship, fitness with recognition, fitness with achievement?

Your body enjoys the exercise whether you do it alone or with somebody; whether you run at your own stress-free pace or strain in competition. It is your mind and your emotional needs that should direct the social side of your exercise. Your running is a mind-body experience. Think about how you will get the most out of it.

Notes

1. Komi, P. "Neuromuscular Fatigue: Disturbed Function and Delayed Recovery After Intensive Dynamic Exercise" Keynote address at the World Congress of Sports Medicine: Orlando, FL. June 2, 1998.

2. Hausswirth, C. et al. "Relationships between running mechanics and energy cost of running at the end of a triathlon and a marathon." *International Journal of Sports Medicine*. 18:5 (1997): 330-339.

3. Neiman, David, Symposium on Elite Athletes, Pre-Olympic Scientific Congress: Dallas, Texas, July 11, 1996.

4. Asp, S. et al. "Impaired muscle glycogen resynthesis after a marathon is not caused by decreased muscle GLUT-4 content," *Journal of Applied Physiology*, 83:5 (1997): 1482-1485.

5. Caselli, M.A. and Longobardi, S.J. "Lower extremity injuries at the New York City Marathon," *Journal of the American Podiatric Medical Assoc.* 87:1 (1997): 34-37.

6. Bam, J. et al. "Could women outrun men in ultramarathon races?"

Medicine and Science in Sports and Exercise. 29:2 (1997): 244-247.

7. Fournier, P.E. et al. "Effects of a 110 kilometers ultramarathon race on plasma hormone levels" *International Journal of Sports Medicine* 18:4 (1997): 252-256.

9

SPRINTING

Many people want to be able to run faster, to play a sport better, to have a stronger *kick* when finishing a distance race or to compete in a sprinting event. While genes play a major role in your ability to run fast, there are ways to train that can significantly improve your running speed. Although sprinting is not a fitness activity, we have included it here for those who are interested in running faster. The techniques and training are rather different from those used in fitness running. Also, do not attempt sprinting until you are in good running condition.

The qualities of a good sprinter are of great importance in the development of athletic potential in many sporting events. In individual sports such as tennis and badminton, as well as in team sports like basketball and soccer, running fast or starting quickly are extremely important skills. Even if you are just running, there is often the need to run faster, to win the sprint at the end of the 10K, for that kick at the end of the 800 meters, or just in a workout in which you are *speed playing* — running with a group slowly, then fast, then slowly. Not everyone has the speed to be a sprinter, but everyone can run a little faster with the proper form and training. So, if running faster is one of your goals, read on!

Fast running is a matter of mechanical efficiency and the speed at which nerve impulses are transmitted from the brain to the muscles involved. Scientists studying the efficiency of movement — the science of biomechanics — continually search for more efficient methods of performing sports activities. There are a number of factors that contribute to the perfection of a running style. One important factor in a good running style is the optimal combination of stride frequency and stride length. Both increase as we run faster, with stride length increasing more than frequency.

Among the variables that can contribute to stride length and stride frequency are:
1. Leg length
2. Muscle strength

SPRINT TIME RATIOS FOR 100 METERS			
First 30 meters: time from starting blocks **Acceleration Phase**	Second 30 meters: **Maximal Velocity Phase**	Last 40 meters	Probable time for the 100 meter sprint
3.7	2.6	3.6	9.9
3.9	2.8	3.8	10.5
4.1	3.0	4.0	11.1
4.2	3.1	4.1	11.4
4.3	3.2	4.2	11.7
4.4	3.3	4.3	12.0
4.5	3.4	4.4	12.3
4.6	3.5	4.5	12.6
4.7	3.6	4.6	12.9
4.8	3.7	4.7	13.2
4.9	3.8	4.8	13.5
5.0	3.9	4.9	13.8
5.1	4.0	5.0	14.2
5.3	4.1	5.1	14.6
5.4	4.2	5.4	15.0

3. Quickness of reflexes
4. The length of the run (marathon vs. 100-meter dash)
5. How tired a runner is

The more skilled the runner is, the more precise the relationship between optimal stride length and frequency is. Because the skills needed and their coordination are rather complex, this chapter will be a bit technical.

The main objective for a good sprinter is to develop the greatest possible velocity in a race. That running velocity is a product of stride frequency and stride length. The aim of a good sprinter is to optimize the relationship between those parameters. In a 100-meter dash, sprinters on a national level use between 45 and 55 strides, and the average stride frequency is 4.5 to 5.5 strides per second. In the 200- and 400-meter events, the stride length is a little shorter and the frequency is slower.

YOUR BODY'S ENERGY

As you know, you get your energy from the oxygen you breathe in and the food you eat. But there are also some body chemicals that are involved in your energy production. At the beginning of an activity, your energy comes from anaerobic sources — sources in which oxygen is not a factor. But within seconds, oxygen becomes a factor and your energy is primarily aerobic (with air). So, while sprinting 100 meters, about 80 percent of your energy will come from anaerobic sources, but the longer your workout or race continues, the more you will depend on energy coming from the oxygen you breathe.

Research results vary somewhat, so the calculations of energy from aerobic and anaerobic sources are not exact. The calculations are that the energy needed to run the 100 meters is eight to 20 percent aerobic and 80 to 92 percent anaerobic. In the 200 meters, the ratio is 20 to 30 percent aerobic and 70 to 80 percent anaerobic, and in the 400 meters, it's about 25 to 40 percent aerobic and 60 to 75 percent anaerobic.

Besides the benefits of the energy capacities and the muscle power (a combination of strength and speed), the regulation of the nervous system might contribute to running performances. So, to enhance sprint performance, you have to develop a combination of physical, physiological, and psychological skills. Your speed depends on a combination of the following skills and attitudes:

1. Reaction time (speed in which the brain can transmit impulses to the muscles)
2. Acceleration ability (how quickly one can get from the start to top speed)
3. Maximum running velocity (top speed)
4. Running technique and coordination skill
5. Curve running technique (running around a curve on the track)
6. Maximal power (muscle strength and speed combined)
7. Elastic strength/explosive power (stretch-shortening cycle potential)
8. Anaerobic capacity (amount of adenosine triphosphate and creatine in body)
9. Aerobic capacity (heart, blood, lung capacity)
10. Flexibility/mobility (range of motion of important joints)
11. Tactics (how a person decides to run the race)
12. Mental strength (dedication)
13. Will power
14. Goal setting

BIOMECHANICAL PRINCIPLES OF SPRINTING

From a mechanical point of view, it is possible to characterize the ideal running technique. But we ordinary people are not robots so there have to be some individual variations according to the differences in body types, physical abilities and neuromuscular functioning. When we look at biomechanics, we are looking at hard science applied to a sport.

Therefore, it gets a bit technical. Just take what you need.

We can look upon running movements as a chain of reflexes. We don't have to think about how to do the sprinting action or the way the muscles should work to generate the optimal power and speed. We should merely understand that the sprinting technique should be smooth, relaxed and natural. To obtain an efficient running movement, the coordination and timing of the muscles' work and force production are of great importance.

The following principles of biomechanics are essential for the understanding of the running movement:

In running, muscular activity serves as a producer of force. In the short sprints, this force can start, accelerate and decelerate in running straight ahead (as in the 100 meters). Additional skill is required when running a curve, as in the 200- and 400-meter distances. In each stride, the sprinter will have a slight loss of velocity in the airborne/flight phase. This loss of velocity has to be compensated by the force production of the supporting leg at the takeoff or push off.

In order to optimize the movement pattern in sprinting, the linear and the angular motions need to be integrated. This means that the specific sprinting movements in the various planes need to be complementary and coordinated, not contradictory.

The body has three axes of rotation: frontal, sagital, and transverse.

- The frontal plane rotation represents inversion and eversion (the downward or upward movement of the long arch in the bottom of the foot).

- The sagital plane rotation is found in plantar and dorsal flexion (the toe of the foot moving away from the knee or towards the knee).

- The transverse plane rotation represents abduction and adduction (the moving outward or inward of the hip joint).

If we take a close look at the different movements in a sprint-running stride, we will see that the legs are extending backward from the time the foot lands until it pushes off the ground at the end of the stride. (Technically, the landing of the foot is called the *front support* phase of the stride, which then becomes the *back support* phase as the hips extend.) After the push off, the leg enters the *swing phase* of the stride. Here, the hip flexes (moves the thigh forward) and the knee flexes (bringing the foot closer to the hips). While the swing phase is happening, the other leg is in its extension or power phase, pushing backward. While the legs are moving forward and backward, adjustments are being made by the hips and the back. The hips move up and down, thereby forcing the thighs to be abducted and adducted (moving slightly out and in as they

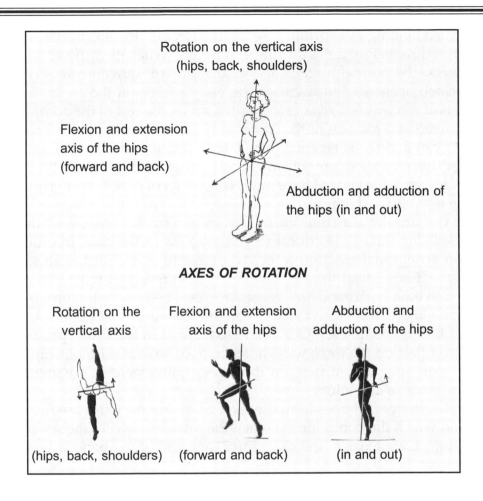

Rotation on the vertical axis
(hips, back, shoulders)

Flexion and extension
axis of the hips
(forward and back)

Abduction and adduction of
the hips (in and out)

AXES OF ROTATION

Rotation on the vertical axis	Flexion and extension axis of the hips	Abduction and adduction of the hips
(hips, back, shoulders)	(forward and back)	(in and out)

extend backward), and the spine is rotating and flexing to each side as each stride is taken.

As mentioned earlier, according to Newton's third law: "Every action has an equal and opposite reaction." In the sprinting stride, the action against the ground in the landing will create a reaction from the surface that generates a force equal to the impact force, which gives the sprinter a forward and upward direction opposite to that impact.

In order to accelerate the body, you must push hard against the ground (action) to develop an optimal reaction force — power or speed. The magnitude of the normal force depends on the force with which a sprinter presses against the ground and to what extent she activates hip, knee and ankle extensors as the leg straightens and pushes backward. If she weighs 120 pounds (54 kilograms), the reaction force exerted on the body by the ground while sprinting will be approximately 550 Newtons. (A Newton is the force needed to push one kilogram forward at one meter per second.) If she weighs 154 pounds (70 kilograms), it would be about 700 Newtons.

When landing in a sprinting stride, the force on the ground can be as much as three to four times the runner's weight. When the sprinter swings the arms, the normal force is also changed. Arm movements serve to alternately increase and decrease the body's force on the ground. The actions of the arms also create forces that act on the rest of the body, such as in creating a rotation of the spine.

We can divide the reaction force into horizontal and vertical components. The horizontal component generates the force that moves the body forward, while the vertical force moves the center of gravity (in the middle of the hips) up and down.

If you are starting from the blocks, as in a track meet, the ability to gain velocity quickly is critical to your success in the race. In order to obtain an optimal reaction force, you have to push hard against the ground. This is called the resultant force. That resultant force is distributed into both horizontal and vertical forces. The horizontal force to get you moving forward is critical. If you get too much vertical force, you will stand up too quickly. Our ability to run fast in the short sprints depends in part on the force we can generate backward with our hip and ankle extensors and, in part, on the lever arrangement in the involved bones, muscles and joints.

In the body, the bones form the lever arms and the joints are the axes around which the bones move. When the muscles used in the sprinting action generate tension and exert force, one end of the bone will move more than the other.

In principle, the longer the length of the lever, the greater the potential linear velocity (speed) at its end. In sprinting, however, this principle is utilized in the opposite way. In the swing phase, the knee of the recovery leg and the arms are bent in order to shorten these limb levers and bring them forward with less energy requirement. If a sprinter has good leverage, she has a mechanical advantage for better and more economical running.

TECHNICAL ANALYSIS OF THE SPRINT STRIDE.

Let us define a running cycle as consisting of two strides — each leg striding once. The duration of a cycle is from the instant the right foot strikes the ground to the end of the takeoff of the left foot. A stride is the movement of one leg from the landing and support phases until the push off is completed. During running, the support phase accounts for about 40 percent of the total cycle time, while the free airborne recovery phase takes about 60 percent of the time.

The following running sequence illustrates the different phases in a sprint-running stride.

Sprint stride

1. Contact phase: The support phase begins with the landing on the ball of the foot, with the foot slightly in front of the midline of the torso until the foot is directly under the torso — or center of gravity of the body.
2. Midsupport: The moment when the center of gravity of the body is directly over the foot.
3. Later support phase and takeoff: The duration of this movement is from the midsupport phase until the full extension of the hip and ankle at takeoff.

In the takeoff and landing phase it is important to work on the following details:

Support phase: landing

- When landing in sprinting, the body has to be in an upright position, with the hip high and a small bend (flex) in the knee and ankle joint.
- The placement of the foot on the ground should be high on the toes, near to the vertical line of the body's center of gravity.
- The foreleg (shin bone) movement should be an active movement down and backward against the ground like a grabbing movement.
- The knee on the opposite leg, the recovering leg, should be in a position near to the landing knee.
- The swings of the arms and legs should be relaxed.

Support phase: takeoff

- To get high force production, you have to contract the hip and leg extensors so that you get a strong push backward against the

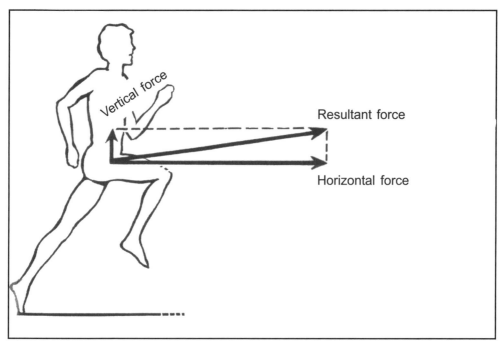

Takeoff

ground with the leg. The hip muscles should start the extension, followed by the knee and ankle joints.

- Get a full extension from the hip.
- It is not necessary to have a full extension in the knee and ankle joints. The knee will stay slightly flexed.
- Keep the body in an upright position, with the hip in a high and forward rotated position.
- The opposite arm to the landing leg needs to have an active but relaxed swing in order to keep the body balanced and to add force to the leg drive. (One of the body's reflexes is called the cross extensor reflex. The arm on one side of the body moves with the leg on the other side. The arm can assist the leg with speed and power movements through this reflexive action.)
- The opposite arm has to be driven backward in a controlled way with the elbow leading the action.
- Look straight ahead and try to be relaxed in the neck and cheek muscles when you are pushing your arms.

Recovery phase/airborne: nonsupport

- The back swing or follow-through: From the time the rear foot leaves the ground (toe off) until the bent knee passes the vertical line of the body's center of gravity in the middle of the hips.

- The forward swing: The forward swing starts from the time the thigh is vertical to the ground and continues with a natural knee lift and forward movement of the thigh.
- The foot descent: The foot descent is the period beginning when the foot starts to move downward and backward toward the ground for the foot strike.

In the airborne phase, it is important to concentrate on the following details:

- The airborne phase is the relaxation period of the running stride. The important thing is to focus on loose swinging movements with both arms and legs.
- At the same time, the body should be kept in an upright position with a little forward lean.
- Try to prevent a backward lean because the force of the push off will move the body more upward than forward.
- It is important to concentrate on the leg action and foot strike in the coming support phase.

THE SPRINT START

Until 400 B.C., runners had to start from behind a fixed line. Later, they made starting blocks out of limestone. The starting position was from a slightly bent standing position. The starting signal was given by shouting or by blowing a horn. According to Andemantus, it was not unusual to punish the one who moved before the start signal. He was often given a whipping.

In the whole history of the short sprints, the runners have tried to develop a maximum force production at the start. To obtain this optimal reaction force from the ground (action/reaction), the sprinters at first had to dig small holes in the dirt for foot supports. The competition rules at that time said that if a sprinter had a false start, he had to move one meter back from the starting line. Then, the poor fellow had to dig new starting holes for each false start. After the third attempt, the runner was disqualified. We can imagine that this starting procedure was rather boring for the spectators at that time.

In the 1930s, the sprinters began to start from blocks made of wood. Later, many types of starting blocks were developed. Today, they are very stable and adjustable. In national and international championships they are designed so that they can register the time and force production (impulse) in the takeoff from the blocks.

THE POSITION OF THE STARTING BLOCKS

Since the blocks first came into use more than 50 years ago, the starting technique has not changed much. Today the most-used starting block positions are:

1. The long starting positions, with the feet far apart: The distance from the starting line to the forward block is between 12 and 16 inches (30-40 cm) and the distance to the rear block is 40 to 44 inches (100-110 cm). The distance between the blocks should be about 1.5 to two feet (45 to 60 cm).

2. Medium broad starting block position — feet reasonably close: The distance from the starting line to the first block is between 20 and 24 inches (50 to 60 cm), and the distance to the second block is 32 to 36 inches (80-90 cm). The distance between the blocks is about one foot (30 cm).

3   2   1

6   5   4

Sprint start (side view)

Sprint start (front view)

CHECKLIST FOR YOUR PHYSICAL CAPACITY/MOTOR TESTS

1. Check your height and weight.
2. Check your leg length and the mobility (flexibility) in your hip/thigh.
3. What is your acceleration ability in 10, 20, 30 yards or meters?
4. What is your maximum running pace in 30 yards or meters with a running start?
5. What's your performance in the 100-, 200- and 400-meter races?
6. Check your :
   - stride length and stride frequency
   - jumping ability in a long jump and triple jump from a standing position
   - maximum strength in half-squats
   - anaerobic capacity in a 200- to 300-meter speed-endurance run
   - aerobic capacity in a 12-minute run. How far can you run?

SELF-TEST ON SPRINTING ABILITY AND AEROBIC CAPACITY

Measure your scores; you will need a stopwatch and a measuring tape.

1. 30 yards or meters acceleration run (standing start or start from blocks)
2. 30 yards or meters maximal velocity run (running start)
3. Long jump from a standing position. How far from the starting line did your heels land?
4. Triple jump from a standing position. How far from the starting line did your heels land?
5. From a start, take 10 strides. How far did you travel?
6. Half-squats with weights; maximal strength test (how much can you lift one time?). Maximum speed test (using half of the maximal weight carried for the one repetition in the half-squat, how many reps can you do in 20 seconds?).
7. What is your time in a 150-meter, 250-meter, and 300-meter run?
8. Run 300 meters or yards three times with a 15-minute rest in between.
9. Run 400 meters three times with a 15-minute rest between each run.

CHECKLIST FOR SPRINTING

Posture:
- Run tall; high hip position
- Feel strong in upper body
- Eyes should look straight ahead
- No downward rolling of the shoulders

Arms:
- Arms swing far behind, with the elbows as high as the shoulder
- On the forward swing, the hands will be shoulder high or higher
- Hands held in a loose fist
- Elbows brush the shirt as they swing by or they can be just wide of the shirt

Legs:
- Work for increased stride length through a strong push-off, not by overreaching forward
- Swing the thigh fully forward
- Lift the knee high
- Run high on toes
- Have an active foot strike; claw the ground aggressively
- To make your strides quicker, envision yourself running on hot bricks
- To keep your stride light, envision yourself running on eggs

DIRECT PERFORMANCE INDICATORS FOR SPRINTERS

1. High stride frequency and average stride length (45 to 55 strides per 100 meters at 4.5 to 5.5 strides per second)
2. Short duration of the whole stride cycle (0.20 to 0.30 seconds)
3. Short support time; ground contact (0.8 to 0.12 seconds)
4. Large upper-leg angle at takeoff indicates a full, powerful stride
5. High upper-leg velocity during the support phase of the other leg
6. Active touchdown with a fast reverse velocity of foot (leg quickly moves from a forward to a backward action)
7. Small foot-to-body touchdown distance
8. Touch down with the heel high.
9. Stiff supporting leg during the ground contact
10. Knee joint stays slightly flexed at takeoff — in contrast to hip and ankle joints which fully extend
11. Small deviation of pelvis from the vertical
12. Small body lean forward
13. High velocity of *snip* movements of upper legs; short distance between knees at touchdown
14. High position of center of gravity (hips) during support phase
15. No rotation of shoulder and hip axis
16. No delay of return movement of arms
17. No rotation of shoulders axis

(Note: Only the first 3 items are relevant. All the others
are not important alone, but are important in coordination.)

3. The narrow foot gap starting position: The distance from the starting line to the front block is 24 inches (60 cm) and the distance to the back block is between 28 and 34 inches (70-85 cm), so the gap is about six inches (15 cm).

4. The *very close* foot position for the blocks: For the very close to the starting line block position (often used by hurdlers who need seven steps to the first hurdle in the 100-meter hurdles), the front block is between six and eight inches (15 to 20 cm) from the starting line, and the back block is about 12 to 18 inches (30 to 45 cm).

5. The rocket start block position: This was a very popular starting position among sprinters during the 1970's and 1980s. The starting blocks were put far behind the starting line. The back block position was 40 to 44 inches (100 to 110 cm) behind the line and the distance between the blocks was about one foot.

RUNNING THE CURVE FOR THE 200- OR 400-METER SPRINT

When starting on a curve, you must put your blocks far out in your lane. This will allow you to run as straight as possible before you must run in the curved path.

When running a curve:

1. Shorten strides on the curve; work for a fast stride frequency.
2. Lean in without losing the balance of your running action.
3. Work vigorously with the right arm and drop the left arm on the bends.

CONDITIONING FOR SPRINTING

As has been noted, sprinters need strength and power in their push off, the speed to bring the recovering leg forward quickly, a strong abdominal muscle group to stabilize the hips — which are the anchors for the thighs — and strength and speed in other areas of the body, such as the shoulders and arms.

Doing half-squats and hip and leg extensions will strengthen the muscles and build leg and ankle power. See the strength chapter (Chapter 19) for the best exercises for these muscles. Sprinting short distances (10 to 20 yards) from a standing or running start helps your overall speed. Running uphill fast also increases your power. If no other exercises are done, just running uphill will increase power by about three percent in 10 weeks. Repeats of 25- to 200-yard uphill runs are recommended. Plyometric work, such as bounding, will also develop leg power.

Strengthening and speeding up the hip flexors, which bring the thighs forward, can be done with the hip flexor and knee extensor exercises shown in the strength chapter. Sprinting downhill, a technique pioneered by the Russian coaches, will help you to make the recovery quicker. This is a major sprinting drill.

Strong abdominals are extremely important in sprinting. All abdominal exercises should be done: curl ups, side sit ups and twisting are all illustrated in the strength chapter.

10
ORIENTEERING

Orienteering, is a sport similar to a treasure hunt. It was originated in 1918, by Swedish scout leader Major Evnat Killander. It combines the skill of map reading with some form of locomotion. While it is generally done on foot — running — it can be done on cross-country skis, on bicycles, in canoes or in any other manner that fits a group's needs. It is sometimes taught at the primary school level, with competitions at age eight. But 80-year-olds also compete in Masters level competitions. It is part of the Para-Olympics for disabled athletes. It is truly a sport for all. There are national championships in most countries as well as international championships. There are also championships for high schools and colleges.

WHAT IS ORIENTEERING?

While first done on cross-country skis, orienteering was soon adapted to foot, which is now the most popular approach to the sport. It has become such a popular recreation that it is now done on all inhabited continents.

The standard type of foot orienteering is point-to-point orienteering. A course of controls (checkpoints) to be found in a specific order is laid out. The orienteer will carry a map and a control card that will be punched with the hole puncher found at the control point. Each punch will have a different pattern so that it can be verified that the orienteer has, in fact, visited every checkpoint.

Lengths of the courses vary from a mile or two for beginners to six or nine miles for experts. Longer-distance events and short-sprint events are also done. Beginner courses are on trails; expert courses are cross country with intricate navigation techniques required. It can be done merely walking the course as a low-energy recreation or it can be done on a highly competitive level. Peter Snell, the former world-record holder in the 800- and 1500-meter events, both of which he won in Olympic competition, is an avid world-class orienteer today — 40 years after his Olympic triumphs.

Another type of orienteering is score orienteering, in which there is a time limit to find as many controls as possible in any order. A long-distance type of competition is called Rogaine. It was originated in Australia. Organized as a score event, it takes place over large areas and for longer periods, usually 12 or 24 hours. Teams of two (or more) navigate over often-rugged terrain, eat and sleep on the clock.

Many areas have set up permanent orienteering courses that can be done by anybody. Competition is not a factor. The challenge is merely to find the checkpoints. In Oslo, Norway, the hills surrounding the city have numerous checkpoints. One can buy maps that will guide the single orienteer to the points. There are so many checkpoints that the search for all of them could take months or years. Both young and old walk or run from point to point meeting the challenge of finding their *treasures* while spending some hours in the wonderful woods.

TYPES OF COURSES

A standard orienteering course consists of a start, a series of control sites that are marked by circles connected by lines and numbered in the order they are to be visited and a finish. The control site circles are centered around the feature that is to be found. This feature is also defined by control descriptions, sometimes called clues. On the ground, a control flag marks the location that the orienteer must visit.

To verify that the orienteer has found the control point (usually an orange and white flag), the control card is punched with the punch hanging next to the flag. The route taken to each control point is optional for the orienteer. In fact, it is the ability to navigate through the forest that is the essence of orienteering.

EQUIPMENT

The competition will generally last only an hour or two, so you won't need much food. But take some water. Bring a compass and a whistle (to signal an emergency). Wear long pants if the terrain is through country with brush or high grass. Running shoes that have nonslip soles and are rugged enough to handle the terrain are important.

Compasses

Orienteering compasses are different from most other types of compasses, such as those used in boating, surveying or the military. In a pinch, any type of compass in which you can see the needle can be used, but orienteering compasses have some other advantages. The most common type of orienteering compass is the base-plate variety. The compass needle sits in a housing in the center, which is set on a clear plastic base plate that you can see through. With this compass, you can set bearings from where you are to where you are going. This is useful for finding places that have few nearby features to guide you.

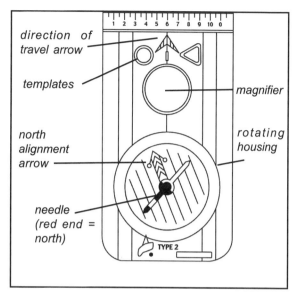

Compass

Another type of orienteering compass is the thumb compass, which straps to your thumb. The thumb compass allows for quick reference since it is held against the map as you go. Some like it for its simplicity; others for the speed of reference in competition. The thumb compass lets you orient to the map with ease but does not let you set bearings as easily.

Use the compass this way: Holding the compass in place on the map, and ignoring the needle for the moment, turn the dial so that the lines in the housing line up with the north lines (meridians) on the map. (The N on the compass and the N on the map should face the same direction.) Make sure that the N on the dial is toward the north (not south) end of the map. Leaving that setting alone, turn yourself with the compass and map until the red end of the needle points to the N on the dial. (Remember, the needle doesn't turn — it always points north.) Once the needle and the N on the compass and the N on the map line up, the map will be an accurate reflection of the terrain you see.

The Map

An orienteering map is a kind of topographic map made especially for orienteering. Topographic means that it shows the shape of the land — hills, valleys and so forth. An orienteering map also shows many other features relevant to an orienteer, such as streams, trails, fences, fields and thick brush. Although many types of orienteering maps exist, most are made to a common set of standards used around the world. Standard orienteering maps are printed in five colors, with each color used for a different class of features.

The orienteering map is central for orienteering. Participants will use only the information provided by the map to find out the control points. Therefore, detailed and accurate maps are essential. In this sense,

orienteering maps are quite different from maps used in hiking or moun-
taineering in the following aspects:

- There is more detail than on topography maps; small features such
  as gravel, boulders, indistinct paths and seasonal streams might
  show on the orienteering map.
- Vegetation, such as the openness of the area, is shown on
  orienteering maps.
- Relatively larger scale and smaller contour intervals (the space
  between the altitude-indicating lines on the map) than would be
  shown on a typical topographical map. The contours might show
  elevations as small as only five meters.
- There are few words, such as place names, and the increments of
  the contours might not be shown.

Map Symbols

The International Orienteering Federation (IOF) established a guideline on the use of symbols on orienteering maps. All orienteering maps
in the world should follow this guideline. Under this guideline, symbols in orienteering maps are grouped into categories and use different
colors to distinguish them.

- *Black*: rocks, cliffs, boulders and man-made features, such as roads,
  trails, buildings and fences
- *Brown*: topographic features, such as hills, valleys, ridges, earth
  banks and ditches
- *Blue*: water, such as lakes, ponds, swamps and streams
- *Yellow*: vegetation that is open and passable, such as clearings and
  fields
- *Green*: vegetation that is dense and difficult to pass, such as thick
  brush or bushes with thorns
- *White*: forest vegetation
- *Purple*: the location of the start, finish and control points

The start is marked with a triangle. Each point you should find, called
a control, is circled and numbered. The control description sheet describes
the feature you are looking for in the circle; for instance: a boulder, a
small hill or a trail junction. The double circle shows the finish. The scale
of the maps ranges between 1:10,000 to 1:15,000. Shorter races generally
use the smaller scale because it is easier to read. The world championships use the larger scale.

Orienteering Terms

Control: the point, circled on the map, for which you are looking. The
    marker, which is usually orange and white, is also called a control

ORIENTEERING MAP SYMBOLS

Rock Features

large cliff

small cliff

dangerous pit or mine shaft

cave entrance

boulder

large boulder
boulder field

cluster of boulders

stony ground

boulder field

open sandy ground

bare rock

Vegetation

distinct vegetation boundary

indistinct vegetation boundary

open land

open with scattered trees

rough open land

logged area (optional)

undergrowth: slow run

undergrowth: difficult

forest of normal runnability

vegetation: slow run

vegetation: difficult

vegetation: tight

vegetation: runnable

orchard

 distinct tree

 misc. vegetation table

Linear Features

large foot path

small foot path

indistinct path

distinct path junction

indistinct path junction

narrow firebreak or tree cut

wide tree cut

railway

major power line (towers)

minor power line (poles)

underpass or tunnel

stone wall

ruined stone wall

high or uncrossable fence

fence

ruined fence

crossing point

Other Man-Made Features

building

ruin

misc. struction

built up area

permanently out-of-bounds area

pavement/gravel

firing range

field grave

cemetery

large water tower

tower

distinct hunter's stand

feed rack

rock pile

trig marker

special man-made object

Leg: the portion of a course between two consecutive controls

Knoll: a small hill

Spur: a small ridge or protrusion on a hillside

Reentrant: a small valley or draw running down a hillside

Contour: A brown line used to show topographic features such as the heights of hills and the depths of valleys

Linear feature: A trail, stream, fence, stone wall or other feature that tends to follow a line. These would be in contrast with point features, such as boulders, wells and springs, and area features, like fields and lakes.

Catching features: a large feature that is not easy to miss in the direction you are going. You might use a catching feature, such as a lake beyond a control, to catch you if you miss the control.

DESIGNING A COURSE

Course difficulties are designated by colors: white is the easiest, yellow more difficult and orange an intermediate-level course. Green, red, and blue are increasing levels of difficulty. Here are some general considerations for the design of a course.

A *white course* is run primarily on trails that make it the easiest terrain to follow. It is a good introduction to those just beginning the sport.

The *yellow course* is designed for males or females who are 13 to 14 years old and for older orienteers who are relatively new to the sport. (It is an appropriate test of skill for the Boy Scout First Class rank requirement.) Yellow offers the beginner an initial experience with the application of orienteering techniques. It should include as many fundamental skills as possible — fine detail map reading, compass, pacing, route choice. Just as with a white course, it is critical that the yellow course be set in an area with well-mapped, clear features. A winning time on a yellow course would be about 40 minutes for a two- to three-mile course.

It is vital to appreciate that, in several senses, the basic difference between white and yellow is that yellow takes the runner from the trail into the woods. The yellow course should be navigated mainly off trails. While trails can be used for a route on a yellow leg, a faster off-trail route should also be available for the same leg. In either case, the first several control points should be found relatively easily. This makes it easier for the participant to become familiar with the map.

Although involving the application of orienteering techniques, yellow should still be an easy course. These competing considerations confine the technical difficulty for yellow to a rather narrow range. This objective is accomplished by the use of a border for much of each leg's length, with a catching feature near each control. The best yellow legs are along borders such as streams, ridges, fences and vegetation boundaries. The legs should be reasonably short — between 200 and 400 yards with a maximum of 600 yards.

A yellow course should be able to be completed without the use of a compass. A leg where use of a compass will result in a faster route is appropriate; however, that leg must have a reasonable route where a compass is not required. Where a shortcut through the woods is an option, it should not be more than about 200 yards and should have a catching feature to stop the participant if he or she has overshot the marker.

For control points, use large and rather obvious features such as a trail junction, the top of hill or the north side of a pond. When a point feature is used, it should be within visual distance of a large feature. Put each control on or near an obvious collecting feature (within 50 yards of one — preferably just after it).

For a yellow course, you would never put a control in a densely vegetated area. If a control is not on a collecting feature, a catching feature must be within 100 meters after the control. Also, you would not share a control or a leg with a white or orange course. Each course should have its own legs and controls.

The *orange course* should be about 2.5 to three miles and will be completed in about 50 minutes. It should be mainly off trails. It should have larger features. Because of its length, it is more of a challenge to one's fitness. It is the same length as the green course and actually longer than the short, advanced brown course.

The best route choices to the controls should invite the intermediate orienteer away from large collecting features (roads and trails) that the beginners must rely on. How-

ever, the penalty for navigational errors should not be extreme; provide attack points and catching features. The orange competitor should be forced to use all of her orienteering skills on the course.

The course should be set so that it forces the orienteer to make decisions constantly. Make sure that the competitor must continue to pay attention and think in order to execute her choice properly. For example, it should not simply be a matter of choosing which one of two main roads to follow for half a mile. The best orange legs require, and reward, continual navigation. A trail or road should never be the best choice.

Mix relatively easier legs, such as yellow difficulty, with challenging legs that are more advanced. Also, mix short (200- to 300-yard) and longer (500- to 600-yard) legs. It is important that the whole course has as much variety as possible in terms of features and navigation problems. But compasses should only be required on a few legs. Map reading skills should be primary.

The control features should be fairly prominent, unless a good attack point and catching features are near. An orange control may be placed in an area of intricate small features, but only if there is at least one and preferably several good attack points to help the orienteers find it, and also a catching feature nearby to which they can rely on if they become confused.

Brown, green, red, and blue trails are the expert level courses. Blue is the most difficult. These trails can run six miles or more.

COMPETITION

If you would like to enter an orienteering competition or join an orienteering club, check the phone book, one of the periodicals mentioned at the end of this chapter or an Internet site. While the sport has a low profile in the United States, there are still plenty of clubs and competitions to join.

If done in a club competition, the organizer of the event will provide the course and the maps. If done in a class, the instructor or members of the class can be assigned the task of marking the course and making the maps.

Most orienteering events use staggered starts to ensure that each orienteer has a chance to do his or her own navigating, but there are several other popular formats, including relays and events in which the orienteer must find as many controls as possible within a specified time.

The course will vary according to the skill and fitness level of the participants. The course will have control points, which are the objects of the search. They are found by using the maps. Each participant will have a control card, which will be punched at each control point. At the control point, there will be a marker: an orange and white flag with a paper punch under it. When the participant finds the punch, the control card will be punched at the appropriate spot to prove that the participant was there. After finishing the course, the participants must return the control card to the organizer. The organizer will calculate their times and check whether the punch patterns are correct. The winner will be the one who spent the shortest time to find each control point and punch the card.

The Day of the Competition

Arrive at the site about an hour before the start. Be sure to go to the registration table first. You will need to pay a small fee and sign a waiver. You will get a map of the forest, a control card and a control description sheet. If you do not have a compass, you might be able to rent one, although you might not need one. A map case (a clear plastic bag) is usually available too so that you can help keep your map, control card and control descriptions clean and organized.

The starts are usually staggered, so your actual start might be sometime after the first starter. After you have been given the preliminary instructions, wait for your name to be called to make your start.

When you receive your map, first orient the map to the terrain by turning yourself and the map until the start is lined up with the route to the first control. Novice courses usually have trails or other similar *handrail* features between controls. This makes it much easier to be guided toward the control point. Choose a route to follow to the first control and check your clue sheet to confirm what feature and controls you are looking for. A control is a set of square flags about 25 cm to a side, divided into a white and an orange triangle. Each control is uniquely identified with two letters or numbers. At the control, you will find a small punch that produces a pattern of holes when punched through your control card. For example, a control with the letters FX might be hanging near a large boulder (the feature). On arriving at the control, punch the control card in the appropriate square to prove you've been there. Then, plot your way to the next control and repeat the process.

Follow all the controls in the order specified on your map. If you get lost (a common occurrence) and find the wrong control, you must go back and find the correct control before you punch the control you found out of order. Also, be sure that you haven't found a control from another course! Start with an easy course until you get your wits about you, then increase the level of difficulty later.

Be sure to check in at the finish, even if you do not complete the course, so that the organizers are not sent searching for you. Check out the results board; results are usually posted as they come in, even for beginners' courses. It is often fun to compare the routes you took with other people who did the course

General orienteering books

- *Orienteering for Sport and Pleasure* by Hans Bengtsson and George Atkinson
- *Orienteering — The Adventure Game* by Ron Lowry
- *Be Expert with Map and Compass: The Orienteering Handbook* by Bjorn Kjellstrom

Periodicals

Orienteering North America by SM&L Berman Publishing. Includes a fairly comprehensive schedule and a frequent beginners' clinic. Currently included as a membership benefit by USOF and several Canadian provinces. 23 Fayette St., Cambridge, MA 02139-1111. Phone:617-868-7416. E-mail: ona@world.std.com

Internet Sites

- *http://www2.aos.princeton.edu:80/rdslater/orienteering*
  Orienteering and ROGAINEing homepage. Lots of local club and federation contacts, many schedules, general info.
- *http://www.williams.edu:803/Biology/orienteering/o~index.html*
  Heather Williams' orienteering page. A good description of orienteering and orienteering concepts.
- *http://www.fi.uib.no/~jankoc/worldo/worldoo.html*
  Jan Kocbach's orienteering page. Many good links to other sites and to maps. Lots of club and federation links.
- *www.news:rec.sport.orienteering.com*
  Orienteering newsgroup (rec.sport.orienteering). Discussions about orienteering, announcements of events, newbies welcome.
- *http://www.orienteering.org*
  The International Orienteering Federation (IOF): United States Orienteering Federation: P.O. Box 1444, Forest Park, GA 30051. USOF can supply the names of orienteering clubs in your area or send you info on how to start a club. Or see *http://www2.aos.princeton.edu:80/rdslater/orienteering* — the Orienteering and ROGAINEing home page.

11

IF YOU WANT TO COMPETE SERIOUSLY

Many women, as they improve their fitness, find a challenge in some sort of competition. Track and running clubs can be found in most areas of the country where five and 10K runs occur nearly weekly. Even women who have reached their 70s and 80s have begun competition in such runs. So, age is not a barrier.

In this chapter, we will discuss competition at a high level. If you are a high school or college competitor or someone who seeks to compete at an elite level, you might find it valuable. If you are a fitness runner or walker, you might find that much of the information is far beyond what you need.

THE QUEST FOR WORLD RECORDS

It often is said that records are made to be broken. As sports science provides us with greater knowledge of effective training, and more people are training harder than ever before, we might expect that world records would tumble every year. This has not been the case, however. Through a projection of statistical theory, Peronnet and Thibault have predicted a progression of women's world records for the years 2000, 2028 and 2033. They did this in the early 1990s. The following chart shows what the world record actually was in 1999, along with their predictions.

Event	1999 Actual World Record	2000	2028	2033
800m	1:53.28	1:51.16	1:46.95	1:46.53
1500	3:50.46	3:47.93	3:38.91	3:38.00
3000	8:06.11	8:11.98	7:50.61	7:48.46
5000	14:28.09	14:19.33	13:41.56	13:37.75
10,000	29:31.78	29:38.41	28:19.04	28:11.04
422,000 (marathon)	2:20:47.00	2:18:43.34	2:12:19.55	2:11:40.91
When comparing the actual 1999 world records with the predictions for 2000, only the 3000- and 10,000-meter times have exceeded the expectations.				

If you are going to race, there are a number of factors that will influence your running times. High-level, effective conditioning is the major factor, but others — such as air resistance and your running pace during a race — can also aid or hinder your efforts. In the information pointed out below, many of the better studies have looked at elite male runners, so these studies will be pointed out. However, typical men and typical women have different physiological makeups. These often show when identical studies are done on men and women. What applies to men will probably apply to women but perhaps not to the exact degree.

AIR RESISTANCE

For men running 800 meters in 1:47, the amount of energy required to overcome the air resistance is estimated to be more than 13 percent of the total oxygen taken in. Of course, the slower the pace, the less the oxygen requirement, and running into a wind greatly increases the amount of oxygen and energy required to overcome the air/wind resistance. High air pressure and low temperature also increase the air resistance.

If you were running around a track, you might think that running with the wind will balance out your energy cost in a race, but it doesn't. Running with the wind only gives you half of the economy you lost when running into the wind. So, for every "2" it costs you to run into the wind, you gain only "1" back when running with the wind. This is probably due to the increased amount of braking force you would need when running with the wind.

DRAFTING

The closer you can run behind another runner, the less air resistance you will encounter. The lead runner will develop a higher air pressure in front of her and a lower air pressure directly behind her. If you were able to run with your chest only 12 inches behind her back, your air resistance would be very low. In fact, you would benefit by being pulled along by a vacuum-like effect from the low air pressure. But even running two yards back will give you some advantage in terms of reduced air pressure against your body. The reduction in air pressure at two yards back is about 40 percent. In a fast 800-meter pace, if you were two yards or less behind the front-runner, your time should be reduced by two to four seconds (four seconds if the pace was 1:51).

In a long-distance race (3000 meters and longer), the runner who is drafting will gain less advantage than will a middle-distance runner. Still, that can amount to a savings of about four percent (34 seconds) for a 5000-meter race, 3.7 percent (1:07 minutes) for a 10-kilometer race, 3.3

percent (2:17) for a half-marathon, and 2.9 percent (4:10 minutes) for a marathon.

Two other factors about drafting: If you are small and you are following a larger runner, your advantage will be increased even more. The speed of the race is another factor. The faster the pace, the more advantage you will get from drafting the runner in front of you.

VO₂ DEMAND (AEROBIC AND ANAEROBIC).

In Chapter 5 we discussed the basics of physical conditioning for a fitness walker or runner. In this section, we will go beyond that information to allow the competitive walker or runner to understand a bit more about the body's needs and responses to training.

Depending on the needs of the athlete, she will want to train specifically for anaerobic or aerobic conditioning or both. If she is a sprinter, her muscular energy will be almost totally provided anaerobically (without oxygen). If she is a marathoner, her energy will be almost completely developed through the use of oxygen in the muscles. This is called aerobic energy development. If she happens to be a 400- or 800-meter runner or a tennis player or volleyball player, both systems will be used extensively. The training for the event must be specific to the way the muscular energy will be provided in the event or sport in which you participate.

To give you an idea as to the amount of aerobic and anaerobic energy that is needed for different events, a study on men showed that for a fast male runner, the percent of anaerobic energy produced decreases as the length of the run is increased. A 400-meter runner (time of 51.3 seconds) would use about 57 percent of his energy from anaerobic sources. An 800-meter runner (time of 1:51) would produce about 40 percent of his energy from anaerobic sources. A 1500-meter runner (time of 3:51) would produce 23 percent of his energy anaerobically. And a 3,000-meter runner (time of 8:15) would use only about 12 percent of his energy anaerobically.

Nearly all energy for muscular contractions is provided for the very small contracting units of the muscle (the sarcomeres) by a compound called *adenosine triphosphate* (ATP). As one of the three phosphates breaks off, energy is released, which allows the actin and myosin proteins in the *sarcomere* to crawl up on each other, allowing the muscle to shorten. This happens in hundreds to thousands of the sarcomeres at the same time and allows the muscle to shorten and move the bones. The phosphate must then be replaced on the ATP so that it can again be released for energy for the sarcomere's work. The ATP is initially resynthesized in an anaerobic way through the use of creatine, which also exists in the muscle.

Creatine is naturally found in meat and fish, but the intake in the typical modern Western diet tends to be only about one gram per day. But the body can use and store about two grams per day. The body can manufacture creatine from some amino acids. Supplementation with creatine is often advised if you are in a sport where anaerobic work is required, such as running less than 800 meters or a mile in competition. For a marathon, anaerobic work is insignificant. If your only interest is in fitness running or walking, there is no particular need to be concerned about creatine intake. In fact, the muscles of endurance runners have been shown to have more than the normal amount of creatine.

For longer periods of exercise, the ATP is resynthesized through the use of oxygen and sugars. Here is a brief explanation of what is happening in your body when you exercise.

The smaller the body and the slower the pace, the less energy would need to be produced through anaerobic methods. Of course, this is dependant on the VO_2 max of the runner. A female runner with a high VO_2 max, for example a 70 VO_2 max (being able to utilize 70 milliliters of oxygen per kilogram of body weight per minute), would need less energy from anaerobic sources when running the same speed than would a person with a 45 VO_2 max. The VO_2 max is a primary determinant for assessing endurance athletes relative to their potential to develop aerobic energy.

OXYGEN TRANSPORT AND USE

1. Quality and quantity of oxygen. Air is about 20 percent oxygen; most of the rest is nitrogen. Higher altitude or lower air pressure reduces the actual amount of oxygen that can reach the lungs.

2. Much of the oxygen that reaches the lungs will reach the small air sacks (alveoli), where it can be picked up by the blood. Much of the air inhaled does not reach the alveoli because it is in the windpipe (trachea) or the bronchial tubes. Of that which reaches the *alveoli*, much of the oxygen can pass through the membrane to the blood. If the alveoli are damaged by air pollution or smoking, they might break down and fewer air sacks will exist. (The advanced form of this problem is called emphysema.) Tars from cigarettes and other inhaled substances can coat the membrane of the alveoli, making it much more difficult for the oxygen to move into the blood. In healthy lungs, the amount of oxygen taken from the air can be 20 times greater during heavy exercise than it is at rest.

3. The substance in the blood that picks up the oxygen is called *he-*

moglobin (iron body). If the runner does not have sufficient iron in the blood, the blood becomes less efficient. This is called *anemia*. It can result when there are too few red blood cells, which carry the hemoglobin, or too little hemoglobin. Low hemoglobin levels in menstruating women are common because menstruating women require about twice as much iron per day as do men or nonmenstruating women. About 18 mg per day is required for menstruating women. It is very difficult to get this amount of iron without adding an iron supplement to the diet.

An additional factor in reducing the efficiency of the hemoglobin is the amount of carbon monoxide (CO) in the blood. Smoking and breathing polluted air increase the amount of carbon monoxide. The hemoglobin binds 200 times more easily with carbon monoxide than with oxygen (O_2), so if the hemoglobin contains a high percentage of carbon monoxide, it cannot pick up the pure oxygen. Nonsmokers living in cities with polluted air have been shown to have between 0.8 and 3.2 percent of their hemoglobin ineffective because of absorbing carbon monoxide. Smokers add another four percent to those numbers.

4. The amount of blood pumped with each heartbeat (the stroke volume) is a major factor in running conditioning. Longtime runners generally have larger hearts. These larger hearts can pump more blood per beat than smaller hearts. Their slower beats allow more time to fill the heart with blood between each beat. While it takes years of hard training to enlarge a normal heart, an increase in circulating red blood cells and hemoglobin takes place almost immediately when one does aerobic exercise if the necessary iron is available to manufacture more red blood cells.

5. The oxygen is then carried in the blood to the organs, such as the muscles, which will use it. The faster the heart beats, the less time there is for the hemoglobin to pick up oxygen and deliver carbon dioxide (CO_2) to the lungs for exhaling. However, as the blood becomes more acidic from lactic acid formed in the anaerobic energy production, it becomes easier for the oxygen and carbon dioxide exchanges to take place.

6. Once arriving near the muscle, the blood in the arteries is dispersed into the very small *capillaries*, which actually deliver the blood to the muscles. Well-conditioned athletes have more capillaries in the muscles they are using in their activities. So, while swimmers would have more capillaries in their upper back and shoulder areas, runners will have more capillaries in their legs.

7. From the capillaries, the oxygen moves to the *mitochondria* where energy is produced for the muscle fibers. The oxygen is used to resynthesize the adenosine triphosphate (ATP), which is the major source of energy for the muscles. The ATP energy source occurs when one of the phosphates of the three (triphosphate) breaks off and energy is released. This phosphate can be replaced either with creatine phosphate, with the energy from the oxygen or through other methods. Oxygen uptake in an exercising muscle can be 200 times the rate of that in a resting muscle. This increases the free oxygen radical production. (See chapters 15 and 16 for more on this.)

8. Another source of oxygen is in the *myoglobin*, a hemoglobin-like substance that is found in the slower-twitch muscle fibers. These fibers can be increased through training.

   So, effective running training, whether for fitness or for competition, can increase the heart size, increase the number of red blood cells that carry the hemoglobin, increase the amount of capillaries in the muscle, and increase the number of slow-twitch muscle fibers that are useful for distance running.

SLOW- AND FAST-TWITCH MUSCLE FIBERS

Runners vary greatly not only in their VO_2 max potentials (the amount of oxygen which can be breathed in, transferred from the lungs to the blood, then pumped to the muscles by the heart), but they also vary in the rate at which the muscles can take up that oxygen (the oxidative capacity of the muscle).

The muscles are made up of different types of fibers. The slower-reacting but high-oxidative capacity muscles (type 1, or slow-twitch fibers) have more oxygen in the muscle fibers, and the muscle will generally have a greater number of capillaries that bring the blood to the muscle fibers. As noted, this type of fiber contracts much more slowly than do other types of fibers.

A faster contracting fiber with less oxidative capacity is the type 2a fiber. And the fastest fibers, the type 2b, have very low ability to use the oxygen quickly. As you run more distance, the faster fiber types become converted to the slower, more endurance-type of muscles. Type 2b can become type 2a, and 2a fibers can become type 1 fibers. So, the more you run distance, the more your fiber types will adjust to being slower but will have more ability to use that oxygen, and your capillaries will increase in number, allowing for more blood to come to the muscles.

Still another factor that will change in the muscles is the amount of oxidative enzymes: substances that might increase your ability to efficiently move the oxygen into the muscles even more than to use that oxygen for energy.

As you can imagine, sprinters have a large number of fast-twitch, type 2b muscle fibers. Marathoners have very few of these but are extremely high in the type 1 slow-twitch fibers. And athletes who train for each distance between a sprint and a marathon have percentages of fast- and slow-twitch muscle fibers to match their training.

TRAINING FOR MIDDLE AND LONG DISTANCES

When we develop a training program, we think primarily of intensity, frequency and duration. Intensity is how hard you run, and frequency is how often you run. Training is frequently categorized by the different levels of intensity. Duration is how long one exercises in a training session.

Intensity

Level 1—150 beats per minute heart rate. This is an ultramarathon pace.

Level 2—150-165 pulse rate. It would be possible at this level to converse with a training partner. This is a marathon-level pace.

Level 3—165-185 pulse rate. This is high-intensity training. In trained runners, it might be used for 20- to 40-minute runs or five- to 15-minute interval training segments. An emphasis should be on maintaining an effective running form even when tiring. This is a 5K to 10K pace.

Level 4— Pulse rate of over 185. These highly stressful sessions should be limited to intervals of three minutes or less. This is useful for training for a 100- to 3000-meter race.

When training at the higher intensity levels, the rest periods between intervals should be longer. Higher intensity work (levels 3 and 4) for four sessions per week tends to increase the VO_2 max. Also, running 60 to 90 miles a week seems to increase the VO_2 max. The highest VO_2 max measurements are generally in male cross-country skiers and long-distance cyclists. The highest recorded are in the mid-90 range while world-class male milers are more likely to be in the low 80s. Women typically are 10 to 12 percent lower due to the smaller stroke volume of their hearts, lower blood volume, less hemoglobin per unit of blood, and the increased cost (due to more body fat) of running the same distance in the same time as men. After age 30, there is generally a one percent drop in VO_2 max for both sexes for each year of aging.

RUNNING EFFICIENCY

Another factor that influences running potential is your running economy. Is there wasted energy in your stride? Do your legs follow a somewhat circular path? Do your arms effectively counterbalance your legs without excessive action? Is your foot placement straight? Does your ankle/foot overpronate? Is your torso carried at an awkward angle?

An efficient runner will use less oxygen and less energy to travel at the same speed as an inefficient runner. Smaller, thinner runners also generally have an advantage because they do not need to exert as much energy to run at the same speed.

The type of course you are running also has an effect on your efficiency. If the course is hilly, you need more power to go up. Then, you will use more braking power when you go down. A hilly course has been calculated to reduce your efficiency by 2.6 percent. This would reduce your time in a 10K race by about 46 seconds.

ANALYZING YOUR BODY'S POTENTIALS FOR COMPETITION

Any doctor or medical lab can analyze some important physiological parameters:

1. The relative volume of your red blood cells (hemocrit) is easily determined. For women, the normal ranges are from 38 to 46 percent, and for men, the normal ranges are 42 to 54 percent. The higher level should indicate more aerobic potential.

2. Hemoglobin concentration in the capillaries gives you an idea of the efficiency of the blood in carrying oxygen. The normal levels for women are 12 to 15.5 grams per deciliter of blood; for men, the range is 14 to 18.

3. Lung function is best determined before and after a VO_2 max test. It can aid in determining the effect of exercise-induced asthma.

4. VO_2 max test is valuable but might be expensive. It should be done on a motorized treadmill, not on an exercise cycle. The cycle is for cyclists; the treadmill is for walkers and runners. An approximation can be gained by using the Rockport test described in Chapter 5, but if you are a serious competitor the actual test should be done. The intensity of the test should be achieved by increasing the speed of the treadmill rather than increasing the angle (uphill running). Uphill running gives an underestimation of what can be realistically achieved on a flat surface. Most world-record-holding males are in the 70 to 85 percent VO_2 max levels. The data for women is more limited but suggests levels of 63 to 78 VO_2 max (milliliters of oxygen per kilogram of body weight per minute).

12

HOT AND COLD, HIGH AND LOW

We walk or run in nearly all temperatures. Because of this, we must be aware of the dangers of being too hot or too cold. We must also recognize the importance of replacing our body fluids before, during and after workouts.

HEAT

Excess heat not only negatively affects performance, but it also can be a source of serious health problems. As the outside temperature increases, it becomes less and less possible to get rid of the heat the body produces when exercising. For example, if exercising at 37 degrees Fahrenheit (3 degrees celsius), you are 20 percent more effective in eliminating body heat than if you are exercising at 67 degrees F (20 degrees C) and 150 percent more effective than if you were exercising at 104 degrees Fahrenheit (40 degrees C). It is not uncommon for the body to reach a temperature of 104 to 106 degrees when exercising. Normal resting body temperature is 98.6 degrees. High heat makes it difficult or impossible for perspiration to evaporate, so the body isn't effectively cooled.

The heat generated in the muscles is released by:
- Radiation: infrared rays
- Conduction from the warmer muscles to the cooler skin
- Convection from the heat loss from the skin to the air
- Evaporation of the perspiration being vaporized

Radiation is the major source of heat release during rest, accounting for about 60 percent of heat loss. During exercise, however, radiation is not a major source of heat loss. But when running in the sun, your body can absorb heat from the sun through radiation.

Conduction occurs through the body's liquids, such as the blood, absorbing the heat created by the contraction of the muscles and moving it to the cooler skin. Water can absorb many thousands of times more heat than can air, so it is an excellent conductor of heat from the muscles.

Convection occurs when the heat near the skin is absorbed into the

Wind Speed MPH	What the Thermometer Reads (Degrees F)											
	50	40	30	20	10	0	-10	-20	-30	-40	-50	-60
	What it Equals on Exposed Flesh											
Calm	50	40	30	20	10	0	-10	-20	-30	-40	-50	-60
5	48	37	27	16	6	-5	-15	-26	-36	-47	-57	-68
10	40	28	16	4	-9	-21	-33	-46	-58	-70	-83	-95
15	36	22	9	-5	-18	-36	-45	-58	-72	-85	-99	-112
20	32	18	4	-10	-25	-39	-53	-67	-82	-96	-110	-121
25	30	16	0	-15	-29	-44	-59	-74	-88	-104	-118	-133
30	28	13	-2	-18	-33	-48	-63	-79	-94	-109	-125	-140
35	27	11	-4	-20	-35	-49	-67	-82	-98	-113	-129	-145
4	26	10	-6	-21	-37	-53	-69	-85	-100	-116	-132	-148

atmosphere. For a swimmer in a cool pool, effective convection is very easy. For the runner, it is more difficult. It is aided by a lower air temperature and by wind. A wind of four mph is twice as effective in cooling as a wind of one mph. (This is the basis for the Wind Chill Factor associated with winds in cool environments.)

Evaporation is the most effective method for cooling the body. Each liter of sweat that evaporates takes 580 kilocalories with it. This is enough heat to raise the temperature of 10 liters of water 105 degrees (58 degrees celsius). As the skin is cooled by the evaporation of the sweat, the skin is able to take more of the heat from the blood, cooling the blood so that it can pick up more heat from the muscles. During exercise, as much as 80 percent of body heat can be released through evaporation. Humidity is the most important factor regulating the evaporation of sweat.

The high temperature developed during exercise, particularly when the sweat cannot evaporate, is a major cause of fatigue. This is particularly true when the body has lost two percent of its water through perspiration. Depending on the person, the sport, and the temperature some people have been found to lose one to six quarts of water in a practice or a competition. We can therefore understand why it is not difficult to enter a stage of dehydration. The combination of dehydration and high body temperature can cause a number of physiological problems such as a reduction of blood volume, an increase in the breakdown of liver and muscle glycogen (a sugar used for muscle energy) and the inability of the body to effectively pass certain electrolytes across the cell membranes.

While it is obviously recommended that people who exercise should replace 100 percent of the fluids lost, it is seldom done. The normal person will replace only about 50 percent during the exercise period. Dehydration of four percent of the body's weight will reduce endurance by 30 percent in temperate conditions but as much as 50 percent when the weather is very warm.

Exercise in cold weather also requires adequate fluid intake. You must warm the air you breathe and your body is still producing heat. You will tend to produce more urine. These factors require you to take in more fluid. If you don't, your body will feel colder because your blood will not have sufficient volume to warm your skin effectively with the heat that it picks up from the exercising muscles.

Dehydration due to excessive heat and/or inadequate fluid intake can cause serious heat-related illnesses. A sudden change in heat or humidity, such as when you train in or travel to a warmer or more humid climate for competition, can cause problems. If you were to travel to India, Egypt or the Caribbean to compete in a marathon, it would probably take 10 days to two weeks to become acclimated to the warmer or more humid climate.

Among the changes that probably will occur in the high heat are a reduced heart rate (due to less need for blood to heat the skin, resulting in less blood flow to the skin), an increase in the amount of blood plasma, increased perspiration, perspiring earlier when exercising, increased salt losses and the psychological adjustments made to the experience of greater heat and humidity.

Adequate fluid is essential to the functioning of an efficient body. When body fluids are reduced by sweating, less fluid is available in the blood and other tissues. These make the body less efficient and, in some cases, can result in serious sickness or even death. To keep the body hydrated, take frequent breaks for fluid intake. However, even frequent water breaks seldom give an exerciser enough fluid. One's thirst does not signal the true need for fluids.

The ingredients of sweat change as you exercise. At the beginning, there are a number of salts excreted. Sodium chloride (common table salt) as well as potassium, calcium, chromium, zinc and magnesium salts can be lost. The initial sweat contains most of these salts but as the exercise continues, the amount of salts in the sweat is reduced because some of the body's hormones come into play. Aldosterone, for example, conserves the sodium for the body. Consequently, the longer we exercise, the more our sweat resembles pure water.

A comprehensive study of blood changes during a marathon has indicated that the sodium ions were not significantly reduced and potassium actually increased. This might make us question the need for these in sports drinks. However, the sugars and water in the sports drinks might be needed. The average marathon runner loses about four pounds during the race. Most of this is water, with some of it coming from the use of sugars (glycogen) and body fats. (About 2900 kilocalories are used in a marathon run.) During the run, the body creates some water as it uses the glycogen. About 36 ounces (1300 grams) are produced in this process. Urination is also decreased, saving the body's water store.[1]

FLUID REPLACEMENT DRINKS

A normal diet replaces all of the necessary elements lost in sweat. Drinking a single glass of orange or tomato juice replaces all or most of the calcium, potassium and magnesium lost. Furthermore, most of us have plenty of sodium in our daily diets.

Fluid replacement drinks on the market are not necessarily recommended. Water, the most needed element, is slowed in its absorption if the drink contains other elements such as salts and sugars. Therefore, water alone is generally the recommended fluid for fluid replacement — and it is certainly the least expensive. For those who want to replace water and sugars for energy, the best drinks are those that contain glucose polymers (maltodextrins). So, if you are using fluid replacement drinks, check the label, then buy what you need — salts and/or sugars. Both caffeine (coffee, tea and cola drinks) and alcohol dehydrate the body, so these should be avoided.

There is no question that if you are exercising for more than 30 minutes, your body will need to take in more fluid. Adding carbohydrates, such as maltodextrins, is highly effective in replacing your body's fuel. In a study of marathon runners given either a high carbohydrate drink or a placebo every 15 minutes during a run, those receiving the high carbohydrate drink were able to keep the blood sugar glycogen much higher during and after the run.[2] Rehydrating with carbohydrate drinks or water is essential. If using carbohydrate drinks, use a solution of two to five percent carbohydrates with maltodextrins (glucose polymers) as a major part of those sugars. During the race, take in about a quart of liquid per hour, preferably spaced at five or six ounces per 10 minutes of running. After an extended run or race, take in about one ounce of carbohydrate for every 14 pounds of body weight in a cup or two of water each hour for four to six hours after the race.

High humidity reduces the ability of perspiration to evaporate. It is this evaporation that produces the cooling effect as the perspiration goes from liquid to gas. This amounts to a cooling effect of more than a half kilocalorie per gram of perspiration evaporated. Exercising in a rubber suit has similar effects to high humidity because the water cannot evaporate.

Wind has the opposite effect. It affects the body temperature by cooling it faster than the registered temperature would warrant. We have all

PREVENTING HEAT-RELATED PROBLEMS
☐ Recognize the temperature and humidity, then take the required measures to reduce injury.
☐ Drink a great deal of water and possibly some fluid replacement drinks during the practice, but don't take salt tablets. Drinks with high sugar content might not be well tolerated by the body. Drink more fluids than you think you need.
☐ Wear cool clothing that allows the perspiration to escape. White clothes will reflect the sun better.
☐ Exercise during the cooler part of the day. Morning is better.

heard of the wind chill factor present on colder days. The wind makes the body experience more cold than would be expected by the actual temperature. (See chart on page 128.) But even on warmer days the wind will evaporate the perspiration and cool the body faster than might otherwise be expected. This might increase the need for fluids to continue the production of sweat.

PROBLEMS CAUSED BY HEAT

If you are concerned about overheating during workouts, it is recommended that the temperature be taken with a rectal thermometer. The temperature during and immediately after exercise should be below 104 degrees. If you were to use another type of thermometer, it would not give a true "core body" temperature because it would be affected by the cooling effects of sweating and other factors.

The best warm weather clothing is no clothes, but unless you are running in a nudist camp, you had better wear something. Changing to dry clothes is not advised because the evaporation effect is maximized when the clothing is wet.

Heat cramps are generally found in the legs, arms or abdomen. The victim will be able to think clearly and will have a normal rectal temperature. The treatment is to give fluids with salt and possibly other minerals, as are found in most fluid replacement drinks. Heat cramps are particularly common among exercisers who are not yet in good physical condition and who are participating in early workouts during warm days. There should be no problem in returning to activity the next day.

Water depletion heat exhaustion is a result of insufficient water intake or excessive sweating. The symptoms might include intense thirst, weakness, chills, fast breathing, impaired judgment, nausea, a lack of muscular coordination and/or dizziness. If untreated, it can develop into heat stroke. A rectal temperature of more than 104 degrees is a symptom of this problem. The immediate treatment is to give water or an electrolyte replacement drink. Severe cases might require intravenous fluid replacement. The skin will generally feel cool and somewhat moist.

Salt depletion heat exhaustion appears to be similar to heat cramps. This can occur when large volumes of sweat are replaced only with water. If a great deal of salt is lost in the perspiration, it can affect muscle functioning. It is most likely to occur during the first five to 10 days of exercising in the heat. The symptoms might include vomiting, nausea, inability to eat, diarrhea, a headache (particularly in the front of the head), weakness, a lower body temperature and muscle cramps. Weight loss and thirst are not symptoms of this problem.

To prevent these heat-related problems, athletic trainers often require that athletes regain 80 percent of their fluid loss before leaving the locker room. So, if an athlete weighed 120 pounds before the practice and 117 pounds afterward, the trainer could require that she take in enough fluids to bring the weight back to slightly over 119 pounds before leaving the facility.

Heat stroke can be caused by heavy exercise just as it can by high air temperature. It is a very serious condition that can affect many of the organs. It can occur when the interior organs of the body are heated above 106 degrees. At this temperature, protein begins to break down and enzymes and the cell walls are affected. When the cells cannot function effectively, the organ functioning is impaired.

In addition to a body temperature in excess of 104 degrees, there can be a rapid pulse (100 to 120 beats per minute) and low blood pressure. There might also be confusion, weakness, fatigue, delirium or the victim might lapse into a coma. The confusion that might be exhibited is often confused with a head injury in contact sports. The skin color is grayish, indicating poor circulation. There might be sweating. The pupils of the eyes might be very small.

Immediate cooling of the body is required when someone reaches this condition. Don't wait for the hospital to treat the victim. It might be too late. Use ice packs to the neck and groin. Full immersion in a tub of cool water is better. One who has experienced a heat stroke should not return to activity for at least a week or two.

COLD-RELATED PROBLEMS

Exercising in cold air might dry out the mucous membranes because cold air cannot hold as much water vapor as warmer air. Wearing a mask that traps the exhaled water vapor and can rehumidify the inhaled air can reduce this problem. However, most problems relate to the effect of the cold temperature on the skin.

Frostnip occurs when the ends of the fingers, toes, ears or nose are chilled. The skin is very cold and somewhat stiff. Warm the body part

Air Temperature	0%	10%	20%	30%	40%	50%	60%	70%	80%	90%	100%
120	107	116	130	148							
115	103	111	120	135	151						
110	99	105	112	123	137	150					
105	95	100	105	113	123	135	149				
100	91	95	99	104	110	120	132	144			
95	87	90	93	96	101	107	114	124	136		
90	83	85	87	90	93	96	100	106	113	122	
85	78	80	82	84	86	88	90	93	97	102	108
80	73	75	77	78	79	81	82	85	86	88	91
75	69	70	72	73	74	75	76	77	78	79	80
70	64	65	66	67	68	69	70	71	71	71	72

Apparent Temperature

Relative Humidity

'Degrees Fahrenheit

Above 130°F= heat stroke imminent

105°–130°F=heat exhaustion and heat cramps likely and heat stroke with long exposure and activity

90°–105°F=heat exhaustion and heat cramps with long exposure and activity

80°–90°F=fatigue during exposure and activity

slowly. Using your hands to warm the affected area is best. The armpits might be used to warm chilled fingers.

Frostbite can begin with temperatures as high as 31 degrees F (-0.5 degrees C). The most likely victims are people who have had the problem previously (a doubled rate), blacks and, of course, those who work or play outdoors in cold temperatures. Frostbite can be superficial or deep and severe.

When frostbite has occurred, gently warm the area. Do not rub it to increase circulation because the rubbing can destroy the cells that have been frozen. A warm bath (104 to 108 degrees F (40-42 degrees C) is helpful. For severe frostbite, the victim should be hospitalized where the rewarming can be done under proper supervision.

Proper protection is essential to avoid the problem and is doubly important to those who have already had one case of frostbite. When frostbite is a possibility, wear layers of wool clothing, vapor barrier clothing, adequate gloves or mittens and a facemask, if necessary. Outdoor practices and meets are not recommended if the ambient temperature is -4 degrees F (-20 degrees C) or the wind chill factor is -40 (F).

Hypothermia is a generalized body cooling. While the cooling is generally not as dangerous to body tissues as is heat, there is still a danger of death. It can occur quickly, such as when a person falls into very cold water, or slowly, when the person is exposed to low air temperatures.

Dehydration often occurs because the blood flow to the skin is re-duced. This increases the volume of blood in the organs. The liver senses the increased blood volume, so it removes the excess water from the blood, resulting in less total water in the body.

Those most susceptible to this type of problem are older people (be-cause of their reduced metabolic activity), young athletes with large skin surfaces but less body mass (i.e. tall, thin teenagers), hypoglycemic or diabetic athletes and those with reduced glycogen stores (energy reserves) due to physical exertion or shivering.

Hypothermia can begin with outside temperatures of less than 64 degrees F (18 degrees C), especially if it is wet. Long-distance races and other endurance events in these low temperatures can cause problems. Swimming, free diving or SCUBA divers are particularly prone to the possibilities of hypothermia because water conducts heat away from the body 32 times more rapidly than does air.

The symptoms, in addition to feeling cold and shivering, might in-clude poor judgment, confusion, muscle stiffness and unconsciousness. If hypothermia is diagnosed, get the person to the hospital as quickly as possible. The hospital can use special internal and external warming methods. However, cold wet clothes should be removed and the body insulated against further cold. The body can be warmed with the victim's own body heat or in a warm room.

Cold-injury prevention is best accomplished by dressing in wool or polypropylene clothing. (Cotton is not recommended because it holds perspiration and increases the heat loss through conduction.) The cloth-ing should be in layers to reduce the body's heat loss and cold absorp-tion through the better insulating qualities of the multiple layers and the trapped air between the layers. You should also wear effective gloves or mittens, a warm hat and/or earmuffs, wool socks and possibly a wool or other mask.

ADJUSTING TO HIGHER ALTITUDE

Running at higher altitudes reduce, the amount of oxygen that is avail-able to the lungs and, therefore, reduces the amount of oxygen available to the muscles. Some well-trained endurance athletes notice a reduction in performance at an altitude of only 2700 feet (about 900 meters). Most will notice a decrease in endurance at an altitude 4500 feet above sea level. On average there is about a 10 percent reduction in performance for every 3000 feet over 3600.

If you are going to compete at a higher altitude, the worst time to compete is between three and six days after your arrival at that altitude.

During this time period, your body is adjusting but has not fully accli-mated. In fact, nearly full adjustment takes about four weeks to accom-plish. During this time, after first becoming dehydrated, the blood vol-ume is increased due to more plasma, and the red cells and hemoglobin increase — assuming that the person has sufficient iron available. So, while each unit of blood has less oxygen available from the air, there are more red cells to pick up the available oxygen. At the same time, the capillaries in the exercising muscles increase so that more oxygen will be available to the muscles. Also, the myoglobin — the iron-based oxygen storage compound in the muscle — is increased so that more oxygen can be stored in the muscle.

Competing in a higher temperature area will also require some time for your body to adjust. But acclimatization to heat is faster than to alti-tude, usually taking about 12 to 14 days.

Elite endurance athletes, particularly cross-country skiers and cyclists but also some distance runners, will sleep at a higher altitude or in an *altitude house*, which gives the effect of being at a higher altitude while the actual altitude would be much lower. The endurance training is then done at a lower altitude. The most effective way for elite endurance ath-letes to get maximum cardiovascular benefits is to sleep high and train low.

Notes

1. Pastene, J. et al. "Water balance during and after marathon run-ning." *European Journal of Applied Physiology*, 73:1-2 (1996): 49-55.
2. Nieman, D.C. et al. "Carbohydrate supplementation affects blood granulocyte and monocyte trafficking but not function after 2.5 hours of running." *American Journal of Clinical Nutrition* 66:1 (1997): 153-159.

13
OVERTRAINING

Long ago, John Dryden told us: "The wise, for cure, on exercise depend." Some people, however, take this advice too far. They exercise excessively and develop health problems as a result of their heavy work schedules. There is no question that effective endurance exercise is a great benefit to the health of the person exercising. It reduces high blood pressure, the risk of heart attack and the risk of some cancers. It also builds up immunity to fight off other diseases. There are times, however, when a person gets far more exercise than her body or mind can handle, and problems are the result. Although these problems are usually temporary and reversible, negative outcomes of physical or mental stress from exercise must be taken into account.

The negative effects discussed in this chapter are most likely to happen to elite athletes or to recreational exercisers who train far more than normal. Those who train excessively are usually in the endurance sports. They suffer from what is called the *overtraining syndrome* or the *chronic fatigue syndrome*. It has also been called *staleness* or *burnout*.

According to the *Oxford Dictionary of Sport Science and Medicine*, overtraining is "a combination of signs and symptoms . . . which typically causes the sufferer to feel mentally fatigued in the absence of physical fatigue." This can then cause deterioration in performance. Physiologically, we often find a higher basal metabolic rate than is usual for the person, a slower return of the pulse rate to normal after exercising, a loss of body weight, a loss of essential nitrogen and problems with the nervous and endocrine systems, particularly the hypothalamus.[1] As you can imagine, these symptoms, which we associate here with physical and mental stress in athletes, can also be seen in the general population in association with burnout in work or home life.

Other symptoms might include any of the following:
- Loss of motivation
- Increased injuries or illnesses
- Loss of appetite, irritability or other mood changes

- Depression, insomnia, nightmares, a loss of sex drive (libido)
- Generally below-average performances

Menstrual problems can also develop. (See page 213.) Any one of these symptoms can be an indication of the effects of overtraining. If the athlete does not recover after two weeks of rest, then the overtraining syndrome can be said to exist.

Overtraining problems are more likely to occur in men running more than 40 miles (64 kilometers) a week or women running over 30 miles (48 kilometers) a week.[2] However, others have found the danger range to be as high as about 100 miles per week (150 to 175 kilometers).[3] The length of the workout, however, does not necessarily influence the intensity of the stress that is experienced.

Athletes often think that increasing the workout will bring increased results. This isn't always true. In one study, doubling the swimming workout reduced the performances of the swimmers. In speed skating, it has been found that practicing more than 15 hours a week is counterproductive. So, if you are a competitive athlete, gauge yourself so that your workouts maximize your performance and don't lead to overtraining and a reduction in your competitive abilities.

Overtraining is often common at the beginning of a sport season, particularly if the athlete has engaged in interval training — short, intense bouts of exercise for one to five minutes each. Long-distance, monotonous training can also be a factor. Varied workouts are more likely to keep psychological spirits up.

Ten percent of the elite college swimmers in the United States have suffered some of these symptoms. This might well be expected since it is not uncommon for elite swimmers to swim four to six miles twice a day during the season. Coaches realize this and generally will taper the workouts as championship meets approach. During the tapered programs, there is more sprinting and far less total distance.

One U.S. researcher monitored the moods of swimmers. If their moods were up, they were given more work; if their moods were low, their workload was reduced. This seemed to indicate that the mood of an athlete was somewhat predictive of the onset of the overtraining syndrome.

Effects of overtraining or overfatigue can be:

1. Mechanical: stressing of bones, including stress fractures, ligaments, muscles and tendons
2. Metabolic: depletion of carbohydrates, inadequate amounts of adenosine triphosphate [ATP], which is essential in the release of energy in the muscles, an excess of stress-related hormones, particularly cortisol, etc.

3. Systemic: involving the whole body or the mind-body relationship such as mental staleness and general tiredness

The amount of time necessary to recover varies with the problem. Bones and tendons take longer to recover than muscles. Replenishing carbohydrates might take only a day or two, but mental staleness might take some time. Effective recovery depends on several factors: age, physiological makeup, altitude at which you are exercising, temperature, and your physical condition.

If you believe that you might be suffering from the overtraining syndrome because of excess fatigue or poor performance, you should see your doctor. It is possible that your symptoms are caused by something other than overtraining. Psychological problems related to home, school or work and physiological problems related to drugs, alcohol or excessive sexual activity can also cause fatigue-related symptoms. So, you might not be able to blame your tiredness and irritability on your exercise program!

Poor nutrition is a common cause of several problems related to overtraining and the female athlete triad. The major problem is generally that there are insufficient calories to replace those used in training. Since appetite is often reduced after training, many people do not take in enough calories, even if they are consuming more than a normal diet.

Reduced immunity

The immune system can also be affected by overtraining. Colds and other minor infections can be more common. This might be because of a reduction of glutamine, one of the nonessential amino acids. (It is called nonessential because it need not be consumed every day — as do the essential amino acids — but if it is not consumed, it is made from other amino acids.) It is essential to your body's functioning, however. Glutamine is an essential fuel for the cells of the immune system. While it is normally released by the body's muscles, its release is reduced by endurance exercise.

Another factor which might be related to the reduction of the immune factors is that cortisol, a hormone which indicates that the body is stressed, is released. This reduces several types of white blood cells, which are disease fighters. After three hours of running, the cortisol level is doubled or tripled, and it stays elevated for about 12 hours. (Forty-five minutes of running, however, does not cause a reduction of the white cells.)

The cancer-killing killer cells in the body are reduced by as much as 50 percent as we age. This is a major reason for the increase in cancers later in life. The running of a marathon reduces these killer cells, but

---

CHECKLIST FOR RECOVERING FROM OVERTRAINING
☐ Replenish carbohydrates in your diet.
☐ If you continue to exercise, make it pleasant (comfortable temperature, enjoyable atmosphere, etc.)
☐ Recognize that if you are older or in poorer condition recovery will take longer.
☐ Recognize that bone and tendon problems will take longer to heal than muscle soreness.
☐ Mental fatigue can be reduced by resting, changing your exercise pattern, or doing exercise that you enjoy.

they return to normal or higher levels within a few days. However, the positive effect of the running increases these cells for long-distance runners when they are resting or running less than 10 miles a day.

PREVENTION

Whether the problem occurs in your exercise or outside of the athletics setting, the first thing to do is to find the cause and eliminate it. If it is caused by your work, change your work environment at your present job or find a more satisfying job. If it is your exercise program, change it. If it is monotonous, find ways of varying your training schedule. You can change how far or how fast you run, where you run or even when you run — anything to make your workouts more exciting.

The major preventive approach is to individualize one's training so that overtiredness does not occur. Planned rests must be part of the training program. When you don't feel quite up to your normal workout, either relax that day, change to another type of program (such as cycling) or merely reduce your normal workout program. Get plenty of sleep.

The basic nutritional needs must be met. You must consume enough protein, fat, carbohydrates and water as well as an adequate amount of vitamins and minerals (see chapters 15 and 16). Carbohydrates must be replaced in the muscles because they are the major fuel in aerobic exercise.

To reduce the chance of bone loss, there must be an increase in calcium consumption through an increased consumption of milk products or through calcium supplements. There must also be an increase in certain essential trace minerals (manganese, copper, zinc) by consuming more meat, chicken or fish or by mineral supplements.[4]

Branched chain amino acids (BCAA) increase the amount of glutamine available to the immune system. For this reason, BCAA might need to be supplemented if you run many miles each week. If laboratory tests show low iron stores, the doctor might prescribe iron supplements. There is no current evidence that extra vitamin or mineral supplements will help you avoid the overtraining syndrome, although they might reduce the effects of osteoporosis.

Adequate rest is another essential. Some people need well over 10 hours of sleep a night, while others can survive on just a few hours. Heavy exercisers generally need more than the average person. Just resting, not necessarily sleeping, is very important for those who exercise for long periods.

Psychological factors are often part of the problem. Problems at home, school or work might reduce tolerance to the physical demands of exercise or the psychological demands of competition. When psychological factors are involved, counseling, relaxation techniques, massage and other stress-reduction approaches might be useful.

To reduce the chances of becoming ill:

- Get enough sleep
- Get enough food, particularly carbohydrates and vitamin C
- Have annual flu shots
- Make certain that you are not losing weight
- Do not inoculate yourself with germs by unnecessarily touching things that might harbor germs (i.e. door handles, passenger handles on buses or trains, faucet handles)

Notes

1. Hartmann, U. and J. Mester. "Training and overtraining markers in selected sports events." *Medicine and Science in Sport and Exercise*. 32:1 (2000): 209-215.
2. Pate, Russell. Symposium on elite athletes held at the Pre-Olympic Scientific Congress at Dallas Texas, July 11, 1996.
3. Kuipers, H. "How much is too much? Performance aspects of overtraining." Pre-Olympic Scientific Congress, Dallas, Texas, July 13, 1996.
4. Saltman, Paul. Speech at Pre-Olympic Scientific Congress, Dallas Texas, July 1996; also Strauss, Saltman, et al. "Spinal bone loss in postmenopausal women supplemented with calcium and trace minerals. *Journal of Nutrition*. 124:7 (1994): 1060-1064.

14

RUNNING INJURIES

Walking and running problems can come from the environment (dogs, slippery road surfaces, ill-fitting shoes) or from the intensity of the exercise (running too fast or too far). Avoiding and preventing injuries is the goal, but when injuries occur, we should be aware of the steps necessary for treatment and rehabilitation. But first, take a quick look at what the research tells us about injuries.

Research on running injuries compiled by the School of Public Health at the University of South Carolina found no major differences in injury rates between men and women; no increasing effect of age on injuries; a declining injury rate with more years of running experience; no substantial effect of weight or height; an uncertain effect of psychological factors; and a strong effect of previous injury on future injuries. Among the modifiable risk factors studied, weekly distance is the strongest predictor of future injuries. Other training characteristics (speed, frequency, surface, timing) have little or no effect on future injuries after accounting for the distance that was run.[1]

A study by the faculty of Human Movement at the University of Amsterdam in the Netherlands, which also analyzed a number of studies that had been done on running injuries, also found that age, sex and weight were not important predictors of a future injury. Other factors found to be not significant included running on hills, running on hard surfaces, participation in other sports, the time of the year and the time of the day during which a person runs.[2] The Dutch study also found that the overall yearly incidence rate for running injuries varies between 37 and 56 percent, depending on the makeup of the runners concerned (competitive athletes, average recreational joggers, boys, girls), and on different circumstances, these rates might vary. If incidence is calculated according to the total number of hours a person ran, the number of injuries has been found to vary between 2.5 to 12.1 injuries per 1000 hours of running.

Most running injuries are in the lower extremities, with a predominance in injuries to the knee. Varying studies indicate that 50 to 75 percent of all running injuries appear to be overuse injuries due to the constant repetition. A recurrence of a previous running injury happens in from 20 to 70 percent of the cases, depending on the study.

From the studies, it can be concluded that running injuries lead to a reduction of training or training cessation in from 30 to 90 percent of all injuries. From 20 to 70 percent of all injuries lead to medical consultation or medical treatment, and up to five percent result in absence from work.

The major factors associated with running injuries are previous injury, lack of running experience, running in competition and running too many miles per week. There is either no evidence or conflicting evidence for the importance of warming up and stretching; the importance of flexibility; one's height; muscle imbalance (significantly more strength on one side of the joint than the other); poor alignment of the knee, ankle, and foot bones; how often one runs (assuming she doesn't run too far with each exercise session); shoes; orthotics; or running on one side of a slightly banked road.

Beginners can reduce chances of injury by starting slowly, which gives muscles a chance to develop the strength and endurance necessary to avoid injury. Too often, an enthusiastic beginner will run too far or too fast during the first days and will develop muscle soreness. Whether you are a beginner or an experienced runner, be aware of the symptoms of overuse and gear down your workouts or rest when they occur. Pain in the knee, hip, shin, ankle, foot arches or toes should be taken seriously.

If you have suffered an injury, make certain that you are fully recovered before resuming a running routine. A major reason for a recurring injury is returning to exercising before the injury has completely healed. Swimming, cycling or perhaps walking can be substituted for your fitness work while the recovery takes place.

SAFETY

While walking or jogging are quite safe for most people, there are environmental factors which might be a concern. Vehicles — both bicycles and autos — can be hazards. Therefore, it is generally best to stay on the side of the road facing the traffic so you can see what's coming. When you see a vehicle, try to make eye contact with the operator to make certain that you have been spotted.

Dogs can also be a problem. When you see a dog, you don't want eye contact because it might be interpreted as a challenge to its canine character. Slowing to a walk while you pass the dog's territory is also wise. If you expect to meet an unfriendly animal, consider carrying a container of pepper spray. It also helps to keep an ear open for sounds of dogs and cars that might signal trouble. So, if you wear a headset to listen to news or tunes, keep the volume low and keep one ear free for safety. Loud music stretches and scars the eardrum, making it more difficult to hear lower-volume sounds. No sense adding your own noise pollution to that already provided by our advanced technology!

In some parts of the country, air pollution is a problem. If this is a factor in your area try to exercise in the morning before the cars, trucks and oil refineries have gotten into full swing. There is always the question as to whether the negatives of air pollution outweigh the positives of exercise. They probably do not.

When exercising at night, wear light-colored clothes and some reflective material. There are vests with silver reflective tape, armbands and reflectors that can dangle from your jacket. If you plan to be in an area that might be dangerous, go with one or more friends and carry a spray. Let a friend know exactly what your path will be in case you are delayed. And, of course, carry identification and some coins for a phone call if needed.

UNDERSTANDING AND TREATING INJURIES

While running and walking are generally safe forms of exercises, injuries might still occur. Some injuries might be suddenly inflicted. You might step on a stone and bruise your heel or pull a muscle while sprinting. You might get a blister. The more common injuries are called *overuse injuries*. The continued pounding on the pavement might cause shin splints to occur in the front of your lower leg or inflame the tissues under your foot — *plantar fasciitis*. Most injuries respond to the same type of treatment.

FOOT INJURIES

The foot is made up of 25 or 26 bones. The bones are arranged in several different arches that go from the toe to the heel and from the great toe to the little toe. These arches act as shock absorbers when walking, running or jumping. The arch that we are concerned with in most athletic injuries is the longitudinal arch that goes from the ball of the foot back to the heel bone. If that is too low, you have *flat feet*. This might or might not be a problem.

The most common injuries to the foot are soft-tissue injuries. The most common soft-tissue injuries are blisters and calluses.

Blisters are caused by an irritation of the skin in which the skin is rubbed and the outer layer of skin separates from the inner layer. When too much friction is put on the skin, it heats the skin and acts like a burn. This causes a blister. The first and second layers separate and the fluid from the second layer fills that separation. The more friction and the more heat produced, the larger the blister. The fluid inside the blister causes pain.

Blisters are most common on the back of the heel, on the toes or under the ball of the foot. Stiff-heeled shoes, shoes not properly laced, shoes that are too large or too small and new sports shoes often cause blisters. Blisters are more likely when you begin something new, like starting to jog or trying a new pair of shoes. It is always a good idea to wear two pairs of thin socks when breaking in new shoes. The extra sock layer absorbs some of the rubbing that the skin would otherwise have to endure. If you notice a special pressure when you are active, paint the area that feels irritated with tincture of benzoin (Tuff Skin), then cover that with a cream or gel, such as Vasoline.

If the skin is continually irritated in the manner that causes blisters, the third layer of skin becomes stimulated and more cells are produced to make the skin thicker. The more the growth rate is accelerated, the thicker the skin gets, and the third layer of skin, which is the dead part that we see on the outside, gets thicker and thicker and becomes what is called a *callus*.

If calluses are allowed to get too thick, too hard and too dried out, they become a source of irritation to the skin below. A blister will form under the callus, and a vicious cycle begins. Calluses should be trimmed, filed or sandpapered, cut or treated so that the thickness of the callus will not continue to cause blisters to form underneath.

If the blisters continue to form and the calluses continue to grow, the skin must be protected against the pressure or friction by padding around that area with a donut-like pad. Cut a hole the same size as the blister in the middle of a protective material, such as a gauze pad, thick felt or sponge rubber. Place this around the blister and put some type of lubricant, such as Vaseline or skin lube, inside the hole. Put another thin layer of gauze on top of it and tape it down. Now, when the pressure comes on

TO TREAT A BLISTER
1. Use a donut-shaped pad around the blister to eliminate any more pressure.
2. Use a skin lubricant such as Vasoline over the blister to protect from any additional friction.
3. Keep the area clean because the blister might pop open on its own, and you do not want to invite infection.
TO PREVENT BLISTERS
1. File down any calluses so that blisters do not develop under them.
2. Always wear socks when you are wearing shoes.
3. Use two pairs of socks, especially early in the sports season.
4. Buy shoes with a proper fit and break in new shoes gradually.

to the upper layer of gauze pad, it will be distributed out and around the blister on to the padding surrounding the blister and nothing will touch the blister. If anything touches the blister, it will be the lubrication that was put between the blister and the top gauze pad.

Athlete's foot is generally caused by a fungus infection. Hot, sweaty, or wet feet lead to a decrease in the acid on the surface of the skin, which it becomes a perfect breeding ground for these fungi. The problem is identified by a burning feeling between or under the toes. In its most severe form, the skin cracks. Common shower rooms are a prime place to pick up these fungi. If you must use a common shower room, wear rubber bath sandals when you shower.

In order to prevent athlete's foot, don't wear tight or ill-fitting shoes or nonporous socks. Wide-open shoes and sandals allow the air to circulate around the feet, and cotton or wool socks help to absorb the moisture. If you wish to wear nylon or synthetic stockings, insert cotton between your toes.

Always dry your feet thoroughly, especially between the toes, after a shower. Use a powder, preferably a specially medicated powder, between the toes. This should be used in the morning, before you exercise and after you shower. Both medicated powders and ointments can kill the fungus. But it is best to avoid the infection by changing socks daily, drying the shoes and using foot powder.

Arch problems affect many people. There are two arches in the foot. One is under the base of the toes (transverse arch) and the other runs from the front of the heel to the base of the toes (metatarsal arch). These arches act as shock absorbers. Extra-high or very low arches sometimes cause problems. An orthotic that is inserted under a low arch will bring the foot closer to normal and will generally relieve any pain.

THE HEEL

A *stone bruise* is a bruise to the bottom of the heel. It is particularly prevalent with those who go barefoot or wear thin-heeled shoes and step on stones. It also occurs with runners and jumpers who continually land on the base of the heel rather than on the toes. Heel spurs can develop because of the irritation. The pain might be quite sharp and might feel like a stone is in the heel of the shoe.

What to do:

1. Use RICE (rest, ice, compression, elevation) for 20 to 30 minutes after exercise or massage the bottom of the heel with an ice cup (a cup of water placed in the freezer).

2. Use a soft rubber heel cup or a donut-shaped felt pad with the hole in the donut directly under the focal point of pain.

3. Do not use heat as part of the treatment.

A *heel spur* is often caused by injury to the heel bone, such as stone bruises. The spur is an abnormal growth of bone that is usually downward from the heel. Many people have these and have no pain. However, they are often associated with *plantar fasciitis.*

Plantar fasciitis is a common complaint, especially with older athletes. It is an inflammation ("itis") of the connective tissue (fascia) under the foot (plantar). It is said to affect nearly 20 percent of runners. The soreness is under the foot and in the heel or just forward of the heel bone.

Plantar fasciitis might occur in several tissues in the bottom of the foot. The most common area is on, or just in front of, the heel bone (calcaneus). The ligaments and tendons that attach to the heel are prone to problems from trauma, overstretching, or tightening due to not being stretched often enough. Tight calf muscles and tendons (gastrocnemius and soleus) are often related to the cause, so stretching of the heel is always recommended as part of the cure. Stretching of the rear calf muscles should be done several times a day. The muscles that move the bones of the foot might also be bruised or stretched.

Another related cause is often that the foot is pronated (the inside part of the foot is closer to the ground). When this is the case, a proper orthotic device that lifts the long arch of the foot might both heal the problem and prevent a recurrence. The orthotic might take up to six months to cure the problem.

The pain is particularly noticeable when getting out of bed in the morning. It might also be evident when standing after being seated for some time. The condition is generally a stress injury where the tendons under the foot are repeatedly stressed such as in running or in doing heel raises with significant weight on the back. Rest is the major type of treatment. A donut pad or a rubber heel cup with extra cushioning underneath might also be an aid. Arch supports, which are made for increasing the metatarsel arch of the foot, can also help.

If you have a continual plantar fasciitis, the insole of your favorite shoes might be worn out. Most insoles of shoes are made for 500 miles of walking or running. The outside and the bottom are made for 800 to 1000 miles, so when looking at the shoe, it might look perfectly fine but the major foot supporting structure might be shot. You might try keeping track of the number of miles your shoes have covered and replace them after 500 miles.

Another way to get rid of plantar fasciitis is the standard treatment: icing after use of the bruised foot, then doing the hot and cold contrasting baths to increase the healing of the tissue in that area. Rest is also a good idea. The activity that caused the problem should be reintroduced

---

WHAT TO DO FOR PLANTAR FASCiITIS

1. Stretch the Achilles' tendon by standing a few feet from a wall and allowing your hips to drop toward the wall. Bend the ankle forward and feel the pull at the back of the heel.
2. The use of a soft rubber heel cup might ease the pain by cushioning the heel bone (and the probable heel spurs) when the heel hits the floor. The heel cup also reduces the tension of the Achilles' tendon and the stretch of the ligaments under the foot. You can also use a felt or sponge rubber donut with the hole surrounding the spot where it is sore.
3. The use of an appropriate orthotic shoe insert might aid in recovery.
4. Softer, more flexible well-cushioned shoes, rather than stiff shoes, are also generally recommended.
5. NSAIDs, such as aspirin might reduce the inflammation and the pain.
6. Don't: walk or run on your toes, walk or run on hard surfaces or walk in bare feet.
7. Exercises that strengthen the under part of the foot should also be done. Put a towel on the floor, and with your toes over the edge of the towel, bring it toward you by curling the toes under and pulling the towel.

---

in a gradual manner. An example would be a runner who normally covers 10 miles a day cutting back to one or two miles daily until the fasciitis is cured. Using orthotics and/or rubber heel cups will help to reduce the chance of the problem reoccurring.

Pump bumps (post calcaneal bursitis) is a common type of heel bruise. The pain behind the heel is caused by wearing high-heeled shoes (pumps) or special sport shoes (tennis, jogging, etc.) that put extra pressure on the heel. The higher heel design of many sport shoes often puts additional pressure on the Achilles' tendon or the back of the heel and can cause heel pain of this sort. In this condition, the area near the attachment of the Achilles' tendon to the heel bone is irritated, causing some pain.

Stress fractures are commonly caused by continued stresses on the foot bones. Long-distance walking or running, especially on hard surfaces, is a common cause of stress fractures in the foot. Jumpers might also develop stress fractures. Ineffective shoes, poor running mechanics or inadequate nutrition can also contribute to the problem. A common symptom of a stress fracture is pain that gets worse with increased exercise.

PROBLEMS WITH THE ANKLE AND LOWER LEG

The ankle

The ankle is composed of a number of bones and ligaments that connect the lower leg bones with the foot bones and give the flexibility to

WHAT TO DO FOR PUMP BUMPS
1. Use an ice cup in a circular motion to reduce the inflammation.
2. Wear shoes with softer heel sections and which do not put pressure on the Achilles' tendon.
3. Use a donut pad over the inflamed area.
4. Do not do exercises that use the calf muscle (heel raises, jumping, running)

move the foot in various inward, outward and up and down motions. Because of the various motions of the ankle and its role in every running and jumping activity, it is critical that we reduce the chance of injury. When injury occurs, it must be treated quickly and effectively.

A *sprained ankle* is the most common type of athletic injury. It commonly occurs when the outside of the ankle is severely overstretched. Because ligaments take some time to shrink back to their normal length, ankle sprains often recur. In fact, 75 percent of those who sprain an ankle will resprain it within a year.

Sometimes, a crack is heard as the ligament tears. Other times, there is only the twisted ankle and the immediate pain. Swelling begins almost immediately. The standard treatment of ice (and, later, heat), compression and elevation should be started immediately. Mild sprains will often be sufficiently healed within a week, so that activities can be resumed. Severe sprains might take six weeks to heal sufficiently.

Lower-leg injuries

Shin splints (medial tibial stress syndrome) are painful overuse injuries in the middle part of the front of the shinbone (tibia). A sharp pain is more likely to be a fracture, but a duller, more diverse pain is likely to be shin splints. These are generally caused by poor leg or foot alignment, by incorrect shoes for the activity, poor running mechanics, running too much (overtraining) or by running on hard surfaces. Plyometrics, such as box jumping, can cause tibial and shin splint problems for both males and females.

To reduce the chances of developing shin splints, wear properly fitting shoes with adequate shock-absorbing properties. The shock-cushioning sole will absorb much of the shock that the muscles in the front of the leg would otherwise absorb. Orthotic inserts to the shoes can also reduce the stress to the leg by holding the foot and arches in proper positions. When the foot is turned inward or the arches are not capable of absorbing the shock of continual running, either custom-made orthotics or commercially made inserts can be a great aid in reducing foot, ankle and lower-leg problems.

The activity has caused small muscle tears, has stretched the connective tissue between the muscle fibers or has been overly stretched and damaged the tissues holding the muscle to the shinbone (tibia). If you can determine the cause of the injury, you can better direct your healing efforts.

Other than shin splints, most lower-leg problems occur in the back of the leg. Tendinitis, stress fractures and stress-caused muscle strains are not uncommon because the calf muscles are used in every running, jumping and dancing activity.

Fracture of the tibia or fibula can occur from a single trauma or from repeated stresses. Stress fractures are more likely to occur as one ages or if one does not have sufficient bone minerals (osteoporosis). The level of fitness and the alignment of the legs and feet might also be contributing factors.

Stress fractures are not uncommon among female long-distance runners. The female athlete triad (see page 213) is considered to be a primary factor in fractures to females. Among both males and females, longer-legged runners are more likely to have problems with stress fractures than are their shorter-legged comrades. And those who run on an uneven or tilted surface, such as on the side of the road where the slope is usually away from the road, are more likely to have problems in the downhill leg. The same is true of running on a banked track. For this reason it is best to balance the leg stress by running as far one way as the other, running on the same side of the street or running the same number of laps in each direction on the banked track. Running on a soft surface, such as grass or sand, significantly reduces the forces that the tibia and the surrounding muscles and tendons must absorb.

Achilles' tendinitis or rupture can also occur. The muscles in the back of the calf (gastrocnemius and soleus) are extremely strong and are used in nearly every movement in which we walk, run, jump, dance or ski.

WHAT TO DO FOR SHIN SPLINTS
1. RICE. Use ice cup massage.
2. Strengthen the muscle by moving your foot upward against the pressure of your hand.
3. Wear orthotics or arch supports (orthotics) and/or better-cushioned shoes. (Commercial shoe inserts should also help.)
4. Don't expect shin splints to heal themselves. They will get worse if you don't correct the problem.
5. If the problem is caused by running, run on soft sand or soft grass rather than a hard track or a roadway.

These muscles control the tension on the Achilles' tendon (heel cord). With every step or jump, we put tension on the heel cord, and problems can result. They might include a single trauma that rips the tendon or a series of minor injuries that develop into a chronic tendinitis. The same kinds of forces that can injure the tendon can injure the muscle fibers and strain or tear them.

Cramps in the calf are quite common in runners, especially during hot weather when excessive amounts of fluids have been lost. In a cramp, a large number of the muscle fibers contract and will not relax. Any muscle with insufficient blood can cramp. For this reason, make certain that you have enough muscle nutrients in your diet (water, salt, calcium, potassium). If a cramp occurs, quickly stretch the muscle. Either have a friend straighten your leg and push your toes toward your knee or face a wall, get your feet as flat as possible on the ground, then bend forward toward the wall until you feel the stretch in the calf muscle.

Varicose veins are not really sports injuries, but they can be irritated by some sports activities. Varicose veins indicate a problem of returning blood to the heart through the surface veins. The blood has been pumped from the heart through the arteries at high pressure to the tissues. It is returned to the heart through the veins. There is little pressure in the veins. The blood from the tissues pushes the blood upward through one-way valves. If the walls of the veins are weak, the blood will tend to pool at the low end of vein section that ends at the valve.

The weakness of the vein wall can be caused by heredity or by standing for long periods, during which the blood pools at the valve and stretches the vein wall. Exercise usually helps because muscle contractions push against the vein and help the blood to move up to the next valve. However, when the veins are severely stretched or rupture, exercise can be painful.

To reduce the pain, you can wear elastic stockings to the top of the thighs. This gives you the effect of stronger skin and reduces the ability of the blood to pool at the valves. Do not wear short socks with a strong elastic top band because it will make it more difficult for the blood to

WHAT TO DO FOR CRAMPS
1. Break the cramp by bending the ankle forward. It is best to have a second person break the cramp for you. Lie on your back, extend the leg up, and let the other person forcefully push down on the ball of your foot to break the cramp.
2. Sometimes the cramp will reoccur shortly. Just repeat the procedure and massage the muscle to increase the circulation.

move past the elastic. When possible, lie down with your feet higher than your heart. This will allow gravity to assist in the return of the blood.

THE KNEE

The knee is obviously an essential body part for running and walking. The traumas or twisting injuries common in sports such as football, basketball or skiing are not a real problem for runners and walkers. Runners' problems tend to come from the overuse of the joint.

A swollen knee might result from any traumatic or chronic injury as well as from an infection. If there has been a break in the skin caused by a fall on a floor or roadway, germs might be introduced. If it is an infection and does not reduce within a few days, see a doctor. You might need special medication to kill the germs. But any swelling can be treated with ice, rest, compression and NSAIDs (nonsteroidal anti-inflammatory drugs) such as aspirin.

Less serious pain can affect every aspect of the knee. Pain in the front of the knee (housemaid's knee or prepatellar bursitis) can be caused by a number of injuries, including damage to the *patellar tendon* or an inflamed *bursa* (lubricating sac). It can be caused by continued trauma to the area or by a weakness of the hamstrings (muscles in the back of the thigh) when compared with the quadriceps (muscles in the front of the thigh) that puts additional pressure on the front of the knee.

Damage to the back surface of the kneecap (patella) is medically termed *chondromalacia patella* or *patello-femoral pain syndrome* but is commonly called *cyclist's knee* or *runner's knee*. There are many causes, including the misalignment of the kneecap caused by a lack of flexibility, muscular weakness in the quadriceps, a bone deformity or by a roughening of the smooth cartilage lining of the patella, which doesn't allow it to ride smoothly in its most desired track.

Patellar tendinitis is common at all ages among runners and jumpers (jumper's knee). The continued flexion and extension of the knee joint during running can cause minute damage to the tendon. In more severe cases, the tendon can tear in the area of the patella or closer to the tendon's attachment below the knee.

Pain and snapping at the outside of the knee (iliotibial band syndrome) is caused when the connective tissue at the end of the iliotibial band is overused and becomes irritated. The snapping occurs when the end of the band moves over a raised portion of the tibia. Poor running technique or too much running might contribute to this problem.

Knee compression sleeves will help to reduce swelling from exercise such as running or skiing. These elastic devices are available at most sporting goods stores and pharmacies. If you have had problems with knee swelling, it might be wise to use these when exercising and afterward. They do not help to prevent an injury only to reduce swelling.

Magnetic knee bands are a new entrant into the injury prevention and treatment arena. Magnet therapy is considered effective in speeding the healing of fractures, but the research is not yet conclusive for other uses. Olympic sprinters have used magnetic inner soles in their shoes to reduce the effects of trauma, so we have some testimonials. However, at this time, there is no scientific data on the effectiveness of magnets.

THIGH INJURIES

Muscle pulls (strains, tears) are common in the hamstrings (muscles at the back of the thigh). The damage might include, or even be limited to, the tendon. The pull is generally high in the muscle near the buttocks. These muscles are commonly pulled during running or jumping events. Often, the victim has not been properly warmed up. Other times, it is the quick change from a lengthening action of the muscle to a shortening action (the stretch shortening cycle). This is most likely to occur when a person is running fast and has to quickly change the direction of the thigh from being pulled forward by the quadriceps to being pulled backward by the hamstrings. The faster the person is running the more quickly this action must occur. The small muscle fibers might not be able to take the transition and might become strained.

Pulled hamstrings are often a result of weak hamstring muscles. When the quadriceps to hamstring strength is compared or when one hamstring is compared to that in the opposite leg, injuries are nearly always to the weaker hamstring.[3]

A fractured thighbone (femur) usually occurs with a single blow, but stress fractures are also possible. Long-distance runners and triathletes are potential stress fracture victims. The stress fracture generally feels like a generalized pain in the thigh and will probably not be as sharp a pain as it would be with a complete fracture.

HIP, PELVIS AND STOMACH

Injuries to the tendons of the hips and their insertions into the hipbones are common in adolescent athletes. A violent contraction of the muscles at the same time that it is being stretched (an eccentric contraction as part of the stretch-shortening cycle) can injure either the tendon or the bone. Sports such as sprinting or slalom skiing in which the legs are forced to move quickly are the most likely causes. Surgery might or might not be required, but four to six weeks of rest is generally mandatory. Treatment will require NSAIDs, such as aspirin and/or ice, and resting in a position that does not strain the injured area.

Stress injuries in the lower part of the inside of the pelvic bones (*osteitis pubis*) are often caused by overuse and repeated trauma to the bones. The continued pulling on the bone by the tendons that attach to the thighs muscles can create such overuse problems. It is sometimes found in long-distance runners and racewalkers. The injury is often thought to be a chronic adductor strain, but it is more serious.

Pain in the front of the hip joint can be the result of a stress fracture, tendinitis (*iliopsoas tendinitis)* or an avulsive fracture. These problems are generally related to overtraining. The overtraining can be the result of too much of an exercise load that is more than the body can stand. This can occur when one is beginning a training program or after a number of months at a high level of exercise.

Bursitis in the trochanteric area (joint of the thighbone and the hip) is often found in long-distance runners, particularly females. This is often caused by poor running technique, especially swaying side to side or allowing the feet to cross the midline of the body. Tightened thigh muscles both hamstrings and quadriceps, as well as tightened gluteal muscles, are often causative. The traditional treatment of ice and heat should help. If this injury occurs, stop running for a time and substitute swimming or cycling for your exercise. Once healed, work on increased flexibility.

Damage to the intestines might occur when there is a lack of oxygen to them during running because much of the blood is redirected to the exercising muscles. Increased fluid intake during running, as well as glutamine — an amino acid immune system stimulant — might reduce any potential injury. Marathoners are advised to supplement with glutamine, because while it is naturally manufactured in the muscles, long runs use up this protein. While it has not yet been determined what an ideal glutamine supplement dose would be, the estimates range from two to eight grams a day with five grams daily considered safe and adequate. It should be taken with about three-quarters of a quart (350 ml) of water immediately after a strenuous workout or a long competitive run. Oats are also a good source of glutamine.

STANDARD TREATMENT FOR INJURIES

The purpose of standard treatment is to stop the swelling and stop unwanted scar tissue from developing. (In some injuries, scar tissue is desired because the scar can protect the area which was injured, but an excess of scar tissue reduces flexibility.)[4]

Most sports injury specialists agree that swelling and pain need to be reduced. Just think of the acronym RICE, which stands for *rest, ice, compression* and *elevation*. Most injuries require this RICE treatment, which is designed to reduce swelling.

The application of cold compresses or ice is called for in most injuries in order to stop or slow any internal or external bleeding. Sometimes, the area affected (hand, arm, foot, leg) can be immersed in cold water. Sometimes, ice can be applied. The ice can surround the joint, in the case of treatment for a sprain, or it might be applied by rubbing a pulled muscle with an ice cup — a cup of water frozen in a freezer. As the ice melts, the paper of the cup is torn away, exposing more ice.

Compression can be accomplished with the hand or by applying an elastic band, such as an Ace bandage, or elastic tape. Elevating the injury to above the level of the heart can reduce the amount of fluid that can be pumped into the injured area. However, recent studies at the University of Texas indicate that some inflammation might be desirable, because the increased blood flow can help to remove dead tissue.[5] Application of heat later in the treatment sequence can also do this.

While the RICE treatment seems to be universally recommended for first aid and for the early treatment of the injury, the next steps to take, after any bleeding has stopped, have less than universal affirmation. After the inflammation has been controlled and the internal bleeding stopped, stretching is generally recommended. The muscles around the joint, or the injured muscles, need to be strengthened. A joint injury can be stretched and strengthened earlier than can an injury to a muscle. Doctors also generally advocate nonsteroidal anti-inflammatory drugs (NSAIDs), such as aspirin, to relieve the pain and aid in the reduction of inflammation. Heat, either by hot water, hot packs, ultrasound or another modality is often advised.[6] A competent sports injury specialist can advise you on when to start each type of healing treatment.

What follows is a common method of treatment for most common injuries. This treatment includes a combination of cold (to reduce swelling) and warm (to increase healing). The number of days in each phase can vary depending on the severity of the injury and the physical condition of the injured person.

Phase One: The goal in the first three days is to stop and reduce the swelling. It is better to completely enclose the entire injured area. A sprained ankle could be put into a bucket filled with ice water. A knee would need a larger enclosure. A bathtub would do. The water should be between 55 and 60 degrees Fahrenheit (13 to 15 degrees celsius). The very cold water will reduce the blood circulation, thereby reducing swelling and scarring. The amount of time needed for maximum effectiveness of the treatment varies. While all body parts have not been studied, it has been found that if a knee is iced for five minutes, it is effective, but 25 minutes is four times more effective in decreasing the blood flow to the knee.

Apply ice or ice water for 20 minutes every two hours and if neces-sary, continue this treatment for 72 hours. If after 24 hours the swelling has gone down or remained the same, the next step in the treatment would be to begin heat, which promotes healing. (Ice does not promote healing but does stop swelling). If the swelling is stopped in the first 24-to-72-hour period, continuing to apply cold to the area is acceptable, but it delays the opportunity to begin healing with the proper use of heat.

The body usually gets rid of much of the swelling before it begins to heal the injury area. If there is a lot of swelling, the body will take a longer period of time to begin the healing process. This is a slight exag-geration as to how the body actually works, but the more swelling there is, the less healing will take place in the area of the injury. The goal is to stop the swelling as much as possible before adding the heat, which will help to heal the injury.

Phase Two: The second three-day period is used to both reduce swell-ing and to promote healing. It is best to submerge the injured area in hot water, but hot packs can also be used.[7] While the injured area is in the hot water, the blood vessels are opening, bringing all the nutrients and enzymes into the area and beginning the healing process. Heat should be about 105 to 110 degrees F (41 to 44 degrees C). It should not be ap-plied for too long a period of time.

The standard treatment in the second 72-hour period would be one minute hot, three minutes cold, alternating five times and ending with five minutes of ice to shut down any blood vessels that might have opened due to the heat and begun bleeding again.

Phase Three: The third three-day period emphasizes increased heal-ing with more use of heat. During this period of treatment, you will subtract one minute from the cold water and add that minute to the hot water so that there will be two minutes in the hot water and then two minutes in the cold. Alternate this treatment five times, ending with five minutes of cold to shut down the blood vessels that are still not com-pletely healed.

This should be done two to five times a day, if possible. If your daily schedule doesn't permit this exact routine, make a few adjustments in order to maximize your healing process. An example would be to get up a half-hour earlier in the morning. Treat your injury once before going to the office or to school. If you have a break during the morning, give it another treatment. You might need to use hot packs (which can be heated in a small pan of water) and cold packs (ice cubes or a pack that can be put in the freezer) at this time.

Lunchtime presents another opportunity for treatment. Repeat after school or work and before you begin your exercise program. (If you exercise, do not repeat the program immediately after the practice. Rather, use ice or cold water to reduce any swelling caused by the practice.)

Your last treatment of hot and cold will be just before bedtime. This schedule would give you five treatments, even during a busy day. But remember, the more times the hot and cold treatment is done, the more the healing process is accelerated. This hot and cold treatment is done for 72 hours.

Phase Four: The routine for the fourth three-day period is three minutes hot, one minute cold. Alternate five times, ending with five minutes of cold five times a day. At the end of the fourth 72-hour time period, and the treatment is 10 minutes of hot treatment four to five times a day. Do not try to accelerate the treatment by using more than 10 minutes because problems, such as unwanted swelling, are more likely.

If you notice any swelling, go back to the previous 72-hour time period recommendations. Cut down on the heat and add more cold to control the swelling. If necessary, go all the way back to one minute of hot and three minutes of cold — the routine for the second 72-hour period — and work back up again. After 24 days, you should be nearly back to normal.

Additional therapy during this time should include exercises. These should be begun as soon as possible after the injury. The earlier you begin with the exercises, the less scar tissue will be formed. While the injured area, particularly a joint, is being iced, move it through a full range of movement.

Let us assume that your ankle has been sprained. Check the range of motion to see how far you can move the ankle in every direction. Take the ball of the foot and press the foot upwar (this is called a flexing direction), then move it downward, then move the foot inward so that the sole of the foot is facing toward the other foot. Then, roll the foot outward so that the sole is facing away from the other foot.

During the first 72 hours, do these movements 10 times during the icing phase of your treatment. In the second 72-hour period, while doing three minutes of ice, do a great deal of movement of the joint. Because the ice is shutting down the blood vessels, the swelling can be controlled.

The standard treatment will help pulled muscles, twisted knees, twisted or sprained ankles, elbow problems, shoulder injuries and lower-back pain due to injury. It will not affect a broken arm. No matter how much heat is applied, it will still take four to six weeks to heal.

Moving more quickly through the phases is possible if the injury is mild and if you are well-trained, because the circulatory system is usually more efficient, so the enzymes and nutrients are brought to the in-

---

STANDARD TREATMENT FOR ALL INJURIES EXCEPT FRACTURES

First 3 days: Icing for 20 minutes every 2 hours
(If it is a joint injury, begin manipulating the joint during the cold treatment.)
Second 3 days: 1 minute hot, 3 minutes cold
Third 3 days: 2 minutes hot, 2 minutes cold
Fourth 3 days: 3 minutes hot, 1 minute cold
Thereafter: 10 minutes hot
When there is no swelling, increase the heat to 20 minutes per session.

(Check with a sports medicine specialist to determine
whether or not heat is advised in treating your injury.)

---

jury quickly and continuously. On the other hand, a person who is in poor physical condition might have to go through the phases as three-day periods.

Standard treatment and rehabilitation principles apply for each joint. Keep the swelling down and break up the scar tissue. Remember that when breaking down the scar tissue, swelling might occur.

PROTECTING THE INJURY

Protecting an injured area is important if you plan to continue walking or running while the injury heals. When an injury is to soft tissue, such as the skin, a donut-type of pad is used to keep the pressure off of the injury and distribute it to the surrounding tissue. Injuries ranging from blisters to large muscle bruises can be protected. Depending on the size of the injury, an appropriately thick pad is used.

For a small blister, perhaps a few thicknesses of gauze pads will do. To protect a larger area, a thick felt or heavy sponge-rubber donut will work. Athletic training suppliers, pharmacies and many sporting goods stores usually have round or oval-shaped pads specifically made for such protection. This will then be covered with a thicker pad that protects the injury and directs any weight to the underlying donut. When protected in this way, the injury is not further irritated.

FINDING THE BEST PROFESSIONAL TREATMENT

A good doctor who specializes in sports medicine is generally your best bet for effective treatment. Not all doctors understand the most effective methods to get you back on the road or track quickly. For back injuries, an effective chiropractor can work wonders. It is generally best, however, to work with a sports medicine specialist. Sometimes podiatrists can help with foot problems. For pain, acupuncture often works. A number of medical doctors have taken special training in acupuncture.

Magnet therapy also often works, especially to speed the healing of fractures. Of course, a trained physical therapist or certified athletic trainer can also help greatly.

Notes

1. Macera, C.A. "Lower extremity injuries in runners. Advances in prediction." *Sports Medicine 13:1* (1992): 50-57.

2. van Mechelen, W. "Running injuries. A review of the epidemiological literature." *Sports Medicine.* 14:5 (1992): 320-335.

3. Orchard, J. et al "Preseason hamstring muscle weakness associated with hamstring muscle injury" *American Journal of Sports Medicine*, 2 (1997):81.

4. Kujala, U.M., S. Orava, M. Jarvinen. "Hamstring injuries. Current trends in treatment and prevention." *Sports Medicine* 23:6 (1997): 397-404.

5. Clanton, T.O., K.J. Coupe . "Hamstring strains in athletes: diagnosis and treatment." *Jour Amer Acad Orthop Surg* 6:4 (1998): 237-248.

6. O'Connor, B., R. Budgett., C. Wells, and J. Lewis. *Prevention and Treatment of Athletic Injuries.* United Kingdom: Crowood Press, 1998; Pfeiffer, R. and B. Mangus. *Concepts of Athletic Training.* Boston: Jones and Bartlett Publishers, 1995, Kibler, B. [Ed] *ACSM's Handbook for the Team Physician*, Baltimore: Williams & Wilkins, 1996.

7. Kibler, B. [Ed] ACSM's *Handbook for the Team Physician*, Baltimore: Williams & Wilkins, 1996. 375.

15
NUTRITION

While most of this book deals with exercise, in order to live fully we must also be aware of our nutrition and diet. A long and full life requires exercise, an adequate diet and play — both physical and mental. The chapters on general nutrition will point out some of the relationships between food and exercise, providing a more complete picture of living healthfully.

NUTRITION

A basic understanding of the science of nutrition is essential to healthy living. An informed person is aware of the nutrients necessary for minimal function and then puts that knowledge into practice by developing a proper diet. Unfortunately, very few of our citizens consume even the minimum amounts of each of the necessary nutrients: protein, fat, carbohydrates, vitamins, minerals and water (the essential nonnutrient). The first three nutrients listed (protein, fat, carbohydrates) bring with them the energy required to keep us alive in addition to other specific contributions to our bodies. Vitamins and minerals will be discussed in the next chapter.

The calorie used in counting food energy is really a kilocalorie, 1000 times larger than the calorie used as a measurement of heat in chemistry class. In one food calorie (kilocalorie), there is enough energy to heat one kilogram of water one degree Celsius or to lift 3000 pounds of weight one foot high. So, those little calories you see listed on the cookie packages you buy pack a lot of energy.

Most people need about 10 calories per pound each day just to stay alive. If you plan to do something other than just lie in bed all day, you might need about 17 calories per pound of body weight per day in order to keep yourself going. An aggressive running or walking program can require even more, unless you are trying to lose weight.

When you run, you use almost a kilocalorie per kilogram of body weight per kilometer or about three-quarters of a kilocalorie per pound per mile. A 170-pound (77 kg) person using 17 calories per pound would

---

ESSENTIAL AMINO ACIDS AND WHERE TO GET THEM
• Isoleucine: fish, beef, organ meats, eggs, shellfish, whole wheat, soya, milk
• Leucine: beef, fish, organ meats, eggs, soya, shellfish, whole wheat, milk, liver
• Lysine: fish, beef, organ meats, shellfish, eggs, soya, milk, liver
• Methionine: fish, beef, shellfish, eggs, milk, liver, whole wheat, cheese
• Phenylalanine: beef, fish eggs, whole wheat, shellfish, organ meats, soya, milk
• Threonine: fish, beef, organ meats, eggs, shellfish, soya, liver
• Tryptophan: soy milk, fish, beef, soy flour, organ meats, shell fish, eggs
• Valine: beef, fish, organ meats, eggs, soya, milk, whole wheat, liver

Cystine is a nonessential amino acid that can be ingested or can be made from methionine. Thus, the two are often listed together.

burn about 2900 calories in a day. This is approximately the same number of calories burned when running a marathon.

PROTEIN

Protein is made of 22 amino acids. These are made up of carbon, hydrogen, oxygen and nitrogen. While both fats and carbohydrates contain the first three elements, nitrogen is found only in protein. Protein is essential for building nearly every part of the body: the brain, heart, organs, skin, muscles and even the blood.

There are four calories in one gram of protein. Adults require 0.8 grams of protein per kilogram of body weight per day. This translates into one-third of a gram of protein per pound. So, an easy estimate for your protein requirements in grams per day would be to divide your body weight by three. For instance, if you weigh 150 pounds, you need about 50 grams of protein per day. Children need 1.15 grams of protein per kilogram of body weight. This translates into about one-half of a gram of protein per pound, so an easy estimate is to divide the child's weight by two to determine the number of grams per day required. The elderly might require as much protein per day as do children due to their decreased energy intake coupled by their possible decreased utilization of dietary protein.

Physically active adults have been thought to require more protein than the 0.8 grams per kilogram of body weight per day suggested by the United States Recommended Daily Allowance (USRDA). In fact, most active people need not eat additional protein if they keep 12 to 15 percent of their total calories as protein. Since active individuals need to consume more calories per day than their inactive counterparts due to

The most common protein foods were ranked according to protein quality by the Food and Agricultural Organization of the United Nations in 1957 and revised in 1973. The higher the rating, the better the essential amino acid ratio. That is, more of the essential amino acids are present. According to the ranking, whole eggs have the highest quality of protein with a ranking of 94 percent. Cow's milk is second with a biological rating of 84 percent; fish rate 83 percent; beef 74 percent; soybeans and brown rice 73 percent; white potatoes 67 percent; whole grain wheat 65 percent; beans 58 percent; and peanuts 54 percent.

FAO/WHO: Energy and Protein Requirements, FAO Nutrition Report No. 52; Who Tech. Report No. 522. Rome and Geneva, 1973; FAO/WHO: Amino Acid Content of Foods and Biological Data on Proteins. No. 24. Rome, 1970.

In 1973, the Food and Agricultural Organization refined its findings by rating the quantity of each amino acid in a food. Here is an example of the rankings based on the percentages of three of the essential amino acids:

	Lysine	Methionine (and cystine)	Tryptophan
Hen's egg	167	138	107
Cow's milk	169	79	100
Soybeans	167	67	100
White wheat flour	55	105	86
Mixture of 1/3 milk and 2/3 flour	93	95	93
Mixture of 1/3 soybean and 2/3 flour	93	93	93

From the above chart, you can see that even the highly rated milk and soybeans are relatively low in methionine and cystine. But if we combined them with wheat flour, we can bring their protein quality into the 93 to 95 range. And the flour, which rated 86 percent in tryptophan, was raised to 93 percent.

their increased energy expenditure, active adults who keep their protein intake around 15 percent of their total calories will eat more protein per day, thereby fulfilling their body's protein requirement. Excess protein consumption (above the body's requirement) will be broken down, and the calories will either be burned as energy or stored as fat.

In order to increase body tissues such as muscle, you must first have all of the necessary amino acids. Your body can manufacture some of them, while you must get others from your food. Those acids that your body cannot manufacture are called the *essential amino acids*, while those that you can make are known as the *non-essential amino acids*. During childhood, nine of the 22 amino acids are essential. As adults, we acquire the ability to synthesize one additional amino acid, leaving us with eight essential amino acids.

Amino acids cannot be stored in the body. Therefore, people need to consume their minimum amounts of protein every day. If adequate protein is not consumed, the body immediately begins to break down tissue — usually beginning with muscle tissue — to release the essential amino acids. If even one essential amino acid is lacking, the other essential ones are not able to work to their capacities. For example, if methionine, the most commonly lacking amino acid, is present at 60 percent of the minimum requirement, the other seven essential amino acids are limited to near 60 percent of their potential. When they are not used, amino acids are deaminated and excreted as urea.

Animal products (i.e. fish, poultry, beef) and animal byproducts (i.e. milk, eggs, cheese) are rich in readily usable protein. This means that when you eat animal products or byproducts, the protein you consume can be converted into protein in your body because these sources have all of the essential amino acids in them. These foods are called complete protein sources.

Incomplete protein sources are any other food sources that provide protein but not all of the essential amino acids. Some examples of incomplete proteins include beans, peas and nuts. These food sources must be combined with other food sources that have the missing essential amino acids so that you can make protein in your body. Some examples of complementary foods are rice and beans or peanut butter on whole wheat bread.

Another reason to be aware of specific food combinations is to enhance the absorption of the protein consumed. The person who is aware of the varying qualities of proteins can combine them to take advantage of the strengths of each. For example, if flour is eaten at breakfast (i.e. as a piece of toast or coffee cake) and washed down with coffee, then a glass of milk is consumed at lunch, each of the protein sources would be absorbed by the body at a lower potential. But if the bread is consumed with the milk at either meal, the higher protein values of both are immediately absorbed by the body.

FATS

Fat is made of carbon, hydrogen and oxygen. There are nine calories in a gram of fat. In the body, fat is used to develop the myelin sheath that surrounds the nerves. It also aids in the absorption of vitamins A, D, E and K, which are the fat-soluble vitamins. It serves as a protective layer around our vital organs and is a great insulator against the cold. It is also

		EXAMPLES OF FATTY ACIDS		

Omega indicates at which atom of carbon the hydrogen atoms begin to attach. This can be a crucial indicator of its nutritional effects. Humans cannot make omega3 or 6 fatty acids so we must consume them.

Name	Number of carbon atoms	Omega number in the body	Where found	Food sources
Linolenic acid	18	3	Small part of many tissues	Some vegetable oils (linseed, soy, canola) leafy vegetables
Eicosapentaenoic acid	20	3	Small part of many tissues	Fish, shellfish acid
Docosahexaenoic acid	22	3	Major part of gray matter of brain, retina (eyes), testes, sperm	Fish, shellfish acid
Linoleic acid	18	6	In most tissues	Most oils
Arachidonic acid	20	6	Most fatty membranes	Meats and organs
Oleic acid	18	9	Most tissues (nerves)	Animal and vegetable fats

a concentrated energy source. Of course, its most redeeming quality is that it adds flavor and juiciness to food!

Just as protein is broken down into different kinds of nitrogen compounds called amino acids, there are also different kinds of fats. There are three major kinds of fats (fatty acids):

1. Saturated fats
2. Monounsaturated fats
3. Polyunsaturated fats

The makeup of the fatty acids in the blood will be dependant on the types of fats you consume. A diet high in saturated fats will yield saturated fatty acids. While these are resistant to oxygen — a reduced number of free oxygen radicals would be produced — they tend to harden the arteries (arteriosclerosis), so they are not recommended. Polyunsaturated fatty acids, while protective in terms of hardening the arteries, are most likely to increase the number of free oxygen radicals. This might be a reason that high polyunsaturated fat intake often increases cancer risk while reducing heart attack risk. Monounsaturated fats are now considered to be the most healthy fats to consume because they protect against arteriosclerosis but do not produce the number of free oxygen radicals that the polyunsaturates do. Olive oil, avocados and many nuts are high in monounsaturates.

Saturated fats are "saturated" with hydrogen atoms. They are generally solid at room temperature and are most likely found in animal fats, eggs and whole milk products. Since these are the fats that are primarily responsible for raising the blood cholesterol level and hardening the arteries, they should be minimized.

Monounsaturated fats (oleic fatty acids) have room for two hydrogen ions to double bond to one carbon. They are liquid at room temperature and are found in great amounts in olive, peanut, and canola oils. Dietary monounsaturated fats have been shown to have a more positive effect on reducing arteriosclerosis.

Polyunsaturated fats (linoleic fatty acids) have at least two carbon double bonds available, which translates into space for at least four hydrogen ions. Polyunsaturated fats are also liquid at room temperature and are found in the highest proportions in vegetable sources. Safflower, corn and linseed oils are good sources of this type of fat. Polyunsaturated fatty acids of the omega-3 type, as found in fish oils, might also contribute to the prevention of arteriosclerosis.

Another type of fat that is primarily commercially manufactured, is the *trans-fat*. As people demanded fewer saturated fats in their diets, manufacturers began adding hydrogen atoms to polyunsaturated fats to harden them. If you read the nutrition labels on foods, you will often see *partially hydrogenated, hydrogenated* or *partially hardened* then the name of a polyunsaturated fat such as soy oil, corn oil or safflower oil. In this type of fat, the added hydrogen atoms are on opposite sides of the molecule. This is called the *trans* configuration. Most natural fats have the hydrogen on the same side of the molecule (the *cis* configuration). The trans-fats act similarly to saturated fats in raising harmful cholesterols. Estimates of the percentage of these fats in the diet vary from two to 15 percent. It depends on how much margarine, crackers and cookies one eats.

We eat too much fat. The minimum requirement for fat in the diet is thought to be somewhere between 10 and 20 percent of the total calories

FOODS WITH TRANS-FATS THAT ARE NOT LABELED
Crackers 40%
Chocolate-chip cookies 36%
Vanilla wafers 32%
Corn muffin mix 32%
Stick margarine 32%
Taco shells (baked) 31%
Potato chips 30%
Cake type donuts 29%
(Source: USDA. Agricultural Research Service)

consumed. The absolute maximum should be 30 percent, which is the amount now recommended for the American diet. While we, as a society, are still above this 30 percent value, our intake of fat has been declining since the 1970s, so let's try to keep that trend going. Most of us consume between 35 and 50 percent of our total calories in fats. Also, our typical diet is very high in saturated fats, and which the fats that we want to avoid.

Our high fat intake — most of which is saturated — tends to raise blood cholesterol levels in many people. For those who are interested in decreasing the chances of developing hardened arteries by lowering their blood cholesterol level, it is recommended that you follow a diet low in fat (with the saturated fat intake at 10 percent or less of the total diet) and consume less than 300 milligrams of cholesterol daily. Put another way: hold the total calories from fat under a third of your total intake and eat twice as much polyunsaturated and monounsaturated fats as saturated and trans-fatty acids.

In the past, companies were allowed to merely identify the oil in a product on their labels as vegetable oil. Under Food and Drug Administration requirements made in 1976, they are now required to note whether it is corn oil, cottonseed oil, soybean oil, etc., because some of the oils, even though they are not of animal origin, are very high in saturated fat. Palm kernel oil and coconut oil are particularly high in saturated fats.

When buying foods, especially cookies and crackers, always check the type of fat used. Avoid those with palm kernel oil and coconut oil. Also, be aware of the hydrogenated oils used. While a hydrogenated safflower or canola oil might still have an acceptable fat ratio, a hydrogenated peanut or cottonseed oil might not contain the desired levels of unsaturated fats. Partially hydrogenated vegetable oils might contribute to the development of heart disease. The dietary use of hydrogenated corn oil stick margarine increased LDL cholesterol levels when compared to the use of similar amounts of corn oil, also indicating an increased risk of heart disease through the use of hydrogenation.

Cholesterol in the diet is not as important as saturated fats in the diet in terms of controlling blood cholesterol level. For this reason, saturated fats should be greatly reduced. This means that the major sources of saturated fats (red meats, butter, egg yolks, chicken skin and other animal fats) should be decreased. As an informed consumer, you might want to keep track of both your total fat intake and your intake of saturated fat to become better aware of your potential risk for heart disease. For example, one egg contains 5.6 grams of fat and only 0.7 grams of polyunsaturated fat. An equal weight of hamburger contains 8.7 grams of fat and only 0.4 grams of polyunsaturated fats.

One more note on cholesterol: It is not the total amount of cholesterol in our blood that is the major factor in increasing our artery hardening. Heavy-density lipids (fats), or HDLs, seem to be protective but low density lipids (LDLs). Very low-density lipids, VLDLs, or another type of fat called triglycerides are greatly implicated in hardening our arteries. Exercise such as running or walking utilizes triglycerides for energy and makes a higher percentage of our blood fats the protective HDL type while lowering the LDL type. So, endurance exercise helps in reducing your chances of developing arteriosclerosis and heart disease.

CARBOHYDRATES

Carbohydrates are made from carbon, hydrogen and oxygen, as are fats, but *carbs* are generally a simpler type of molecule. There are four calories in a gram of carbohydrate. If not utilized immediately for energy as sugar (glucose), they are either stored in the body as glycogen (the stored form of glucose) or synthesized into fat and stored. Some carbohydrates cannot be broken down by the body's digestive processes. These are called fibers and will be discussed later. Of the digestible carbohydrates, we will separate them into two categories: simple and complex. *Simple carbohydrates* are the most readily usable energy source in the body and include such things as sugar, honey and fruit. *Complex carbohydrates* are the starches. Complex carbs also break down into sugar for energy, but their breakdown is slower than with simple carbs. Also, complex carbohydrates bring with them various vitamins and minerals.

People in the United States often eat too many simple carbohydrates. These are the so-called *empty calories*. They are empty because they have no vitamins, minerals or fibers. While a person who uses a great deal of energy can consume these empty calories without potential weight gain, most of us find these empty calories settling on our hips. The average person consumes 125 pounds of sugar per year, which is equivalent to one teaspoon every 40 minutes — night and day. Since each teaspoon of sugar contains 17 calories, this amounts to 231,000 calories, or 66 pounds, of potential body fat if this energy is not used as fuel for daily living.

High-carbohydrate diets that are especially high in sugar might be hazardous to one's health. They can increase the amount of triglycerides produced in the liver. As previously noted, these triglycerides are blood fats and are possible developers of hardened arteries. Also, a diet high in simple carbohydrates can lead to obesity, which can then result in the development of late-onset diabetes.

Fiber is the part of foods we take in that is not digestible. Fiber helps to move the food through the intestines by increasing their peristaltic action. Vegetable fibers are made up chiefly of cellulose, an indigestible carbohydrate that is the main ingredient in the cell walls of plants. Plant-eating animals such as cows can digest cellulose. Meat-eating animals such as humans do not have the proper enzymes in their digestive tracts to metabolize cellulose.

Bran (which includes the husks of wheat, oats, rice, rye and corn) is another type of fiber. It is indigestible because of the silica in the outer husks. Some of the fibers, such as wheat bran, are insoluble. Their major function is to add bulk to the feces and to speed the digested foods through the intestines. This reduces one's risk of constipation, intestinal cancer, appendicitis and diverticulosis.

Some types of fiber are soluble. That is, they can pick up certain substances such as dietary cholesterol. Pectin, commonly found in raw fruits (especially apple skins), oat and rice brans, and some gums from the seeds and stems of tropical plants (such as guar and xanthin) are examples of soluble fibers. These pick up cholesterols as they move through the intestines. (Guar and xanthin gums are often used in low- and no-fat salad dressings. So, these dressings not only do not add fat, they actually assist us to remove fats from our bodies.)

Foods high in fiber are also valuable in weight-reducing diets because they speed the passage of foods through the digestive tract, thereby cutting the amount of possible absorption. They also cut the amount of hunger experienced by a dieter because they fill the stomach. A larger salad with a diet dressing might give the person very few calories but still enough cellulose to fill the stomach, cut the hunger and move other foods through the intestinal passage.

Food processing often removes the natural fiber from the food. This is one of the primary reasons those of us in developed countries have relatively low amounts of fiber in our diets. For instance, white bread has only a trace of fiber — about nine grams in a loaf — while old-fashioned whole wheat bread has 70 grams. Also, when you peel an apple, you remove much of the fiber.

Dietitians urge that people include more fiber in their diets. People should be particularly conscious of the benefits of whole-grain cereals, bran and fibrous vegetables. Root vegetables (carrots, beets and turnips) and leafy vegetables are very good sources of fiber. The average diet has between 10 and 20 grams of fiber in it per day. The National Cancer Institute recommends that we consume 25 to 35 grams of fiber each day to reduce the incidence of colon cancer that is more prevalent in the low-fiber consuming countries.

WATER

Water is called the essential nonnutrient because it brings with it no nutritional value, and yet, without it, we would die. Water makes up approximately 60 percent of the adult body, while an infant's body is nearly 80 percent water. Water is used to cool the body through perspiration, to carry nutrients to and waste products from the cells, to help cushion our vital organs, and in the makeup of all body fluids.

The body has about 18 square feet of skin that contains about two million sweat glands. On a comfortable day, a person will perspire about a half pint of water. Somebody exercising on a severely hot day might lose as much as seven quarts of water. This needs to be replaced or severe dehydration can result. It is therefore generally recommended that each person drink eight, eight-ounce glasses of water, or its equivalent in other fluids, daily. This amount is dependent on the climate and altitude in which you live, the types of foods that you eat and the amount of activity that you participate in on a day-to-day basis.

16
VITAMINS, MINERALS, PHYTOCHEMICALS AND ANTIOXIDANTS

Vitamins are organic compounds made up of a number of chemicals that are essential in small amounts for the growth and development of animals and humans. They act as enzymes (catalysts) that facilitate many of the body processes. Although there is some controversy as to the importance of consuming excess vitamins, it is acknowledged that we need a minimum amount of vitamins for proper functioning. Now that the destructive impact of free oxygen radicals (discussed below) has been established, it is generally recommended that certain vitamins be included in the daily intake of these nutrients at higher than the levels earlier recommended. Minerals are single elements found in nature that are necessary for many body functions. Phytochemicals are plant chemicals that aid the body in functioning more effectively.

FREE OXYGEN RADICALS AND ANTIOXIDANTS

One of the most talked about health concerns in recent years has to do with *free oxygen radicals* and their damage to the cells of the body; their causative effect on cancers, heart disease and other problems; and how they can be neutralized before they damage the body's cells.

Free oxygen radicals are single atoms of oxygen that can combine with many molecules and tissues. They are harmful substances produced by many natural body processes. Physical exercise, for all of its benefits, is one producer of free oxygen radicals. So is smoking and air pollution. In fact, normal processes of living, even sleeping, produce some free oxygen radicals. It seems that between three and 15 percent of all oxygen (O_2) goes through a stage where it is a free oxygen radical.[1]

Free oxygen radicals are also found in the environment. Air and water pollution, any type of smoke and even dried milk and eggs are some of the environmental sources of these toxins. The free oxygen radicals are implicated in many diseases, particularly mouth, throat, skin, stomach, prostate, colon, esophagus and lung cancers. They are also suspected of being one of the substances that can start the lesions that develop into hardened arteries and heart disease. They have also been suspected of causing cataracts (a hardening and damaging of the lens of the eye) and infertility. They are also linked to about 50 other diseases, including ulcers, asthma and high blood pressure.

Some possible concerns for heavily exercising runners include lung injury, which can occur when breathing air polluted by ozone. The ozone reacts with water in the respiratory tract to form free oxygen radicals. Naturally, running in polluted air will increase the potential damage. However, the lining of the respiratory tract contains many antioxidants. Because of this, there seems to be only minimal grounds for concern about free oxygen radical damage to the lungs. Antioxidant supplements, however, might increase the natural protection. Other air pollutants such as carbon monoxide and particulates might damage the lungs, and the carbon monoxide will make the red blood cells less effective as oxygen transporters.

Red blood cells pick up the oxygen in the lungs as they release carbon dioxide. This process also develops free oxygen radicals that can damage the cell wall of the red cells and make them more liable to break down, especially when exposed to other stresses such as the foot strike in running. Vitamin E might have a preventative effect here. However, it might increase the oxidative damage to the cell walls even though it is an antioxidant if it is consumed in excess of a gram a day.[2]

The body produces many antioxidants on its own. The biological antioxidant defense system is an integrated array of enzymes, antioxidants and free radical scavengers. For those with a biology background, these include glutathione reductase, glutathione-s-transferase, glutathione peroxidase, phospholipid hydroperoxide glutathione peroxidase, superoxide dismutase, uric acid, carnosine and some enzymes found in the muscles.

The maximal development of these natural enzymes and other factors depends on the nutrition of the person. Proteins, carbohydrates and fats are essential to the development of a healthy immune and antioxidant-protective milieu. Several vitamins, minerals and phytochemicals (discussed later in the chapter) either act as antioxidants themselves or are essential in building these natural body antioxidant defenses. An inadequate intake of the essential nutrients has been implicated with the development of heart disease, cancer, stroke and arthritis.

In animal and human experiments relating to the effect of the antioxidant properties of vitamins C and E against air pollution and smoke, it was found that vitamin C is more effective in protecting against nitrogen dioxide, while vitamin E is more effective against ozone's oxidative effects. It should be noted, though, that for maximal protection against the harmful effects of air pollutants, the recommended dietary allowances for both of these vitamins should be increased.

VITAMINS

Some vitamins are soluble only in water, while others need fat to be absorbed by the body. The *water-soluble vitamins* — B complex and C — are more fragile than the fat-soluble vitamins. This is because they are more easily destroyed by the heat of cooking, and if boiled, they lose a little of their potency into the water. Since they are not stored in the body, they should be included in the daily diet.

The *fat-soluble vitamins* — A, D, E and K — need oils in the intestines to be absorbed by the body. They are more stable than the water-soluble vitamins and are not destroyed by normal cooking methods. Because they are stored in the body, there is the possibility of ingesting too much of them, especially vitamins A and D.

Nutritional researchers disagree as to whether vitamin supplements are necessary. But they are generally in agreement that natural vitamins are no better than synthetically prepared vitamins. Thus, synthetically made ascorbic acid *is* vitamin C.

Vitamin A is necessary for eyesight as well as skin. During World War II, Denmark began exporting large amounts of butter while supplementing Danish diets with margarine. Many children developed vision problems. It was eventually discovered that the lack of vitamin A in the margarine was responsible for the eye problems. The minimum vitamin A requirements, which the Danes had been consuming when they were eating butter, were reduced when they substituted margarine. Vitamin A was then added to the margarine and no further problems developed.

It is possible to get too much vitamin A. When this happens, the liver can enlarge. There can be loss of appetite or weight, loss of hair, severe bone and joint pain and cracking lips. It probably requires 20 times the minimum daily requirement over a long period of time before this would occur. Here we are talking about vitamin A that comes from animal sources such as liver, milk and butter, not the plant sources of beta carotene, which the body can synthesize into vitamin A.

Beta carotene is the plant source from which our bodies make vitamin A. Beta carotene does not seem to have the toxicity that the vitamin A from animal sources has. Beta carotene is a powerful antioxidant. Along with other antioxidants — including vitamins C and E and the minerals selenium, zinc and chromium x — beta carotene donates electrons to free oxygen radicals, making them less destructive. Once the beta carotene is converted to vitamin A, it is no longer an antioxidant.

If you haven't taken in sufficient vitamin A through milk, eggs, liver, cheese, butter or fish oil, six units of beta carotene can be converted into one unit of vitamin A. What is left acts as a strong antioxidant. It can lower the risk of cataracts. It also reduces the risk of many cancers, particularly lung, bladder, rectal and the serious skin cancer called melanoma. There is no recommended minimum daily requirement for this substance, but the vitamin A that it can make has a minimum recommended daily amount of 4000 international units (IU) for women and 5000 for men.

The *B-complex* vitamins include at least 15 substances; only six have been termed essential. The B vitamins seem to work together, particularly in the nervous, circulatory and digestive systems. Since they work together, an overdose of some could result in a deficiency in others.

Vitamin B1 (thiamin) is used to help convert sugars (glucose) into an energy source that can be more readily used in the muscles. For this reason, people who are doing aerobic training must make certain that they have sufficient vitamin B. Without the vitamin, a disease called *beriberi* develops. This disease results in the victim not having any energy.

The primary function of *vitamin B2* (riboflavin) is to help to convert fatty acids and proteins into sugars that can be used for energy. Riboflavin and vitamin B6 (pyridoxine) deficiencies might hamper fitness performance. However, if a person is not deficient, there appears to be no additional fitness benefit from further supplementation of these vitamins. With an increase in exercise training, riboflavin stores in the body have been shown to be reduced. Because of this, it might be necessary to increase riboflavin intake when embarking on or increasing an existing exercise program.

Vitamin B3 (niacin) is necessary for the breakdown of glucose into energy. Therefore, it is essential for endurance athletes. It has also been found to inhibit the growth rate of some cancer cells in rats. Pellagra, a niacin deficiency disease, can lead to the development of symptoms of mental illness, such as hallucinations.

Vitamin B6 has several roles, but its major function is in the development of proteins from amino acids. So, if you are concerned with building muscle tissue it might be an important vitamin.

Vitamin B12 is necessary for the development of red blood cells and for maintaining the fatty sheath that protects the nerves. *Vegans*, those who consume no animal products or byproducts, have diets that are usually deficient in vitamin B12. This is a concern because a vitamin B12 deficiency, in extreme cases, can cause a loss of brain function. Also, a group of vegans in England suffered irreversible destruction of nerve fibers in the spinal cord after 10 to 15 years because of their chronic vitamin B12 deficiency.

Folacin (folic acid) is a component of many tissues. If there is not enough of the vitamin present, the work of the cells is impaired. It is now known that it is an essential nutrient for pregnant mothers because a deficiency can cause severe birth defects in their children.

Excessive B vitamins can affect the efficiency of drugs being taken, so it is important to consider where your diet is in terms of your B vitamins when taking prescription drugs. For example, riboflavin can interfere with the effects of tetracycline, an antibiotic. Pyridoxine can interfere with levadopa, which is often prescribed for Parkinson's disease. And folic acid can lessen the effects of an antiepileptic drug.

Vitamin C is essential in the production of collagen, the protein substance that is the mainstay of the body's connective tissues including tendons, ligaments and other body tissues, such as bones, teeth and skin. It also is important for healing wounds. In addition, it helps the body to use iron, and it assists in the creation of the thyroid hormone thyroxin. It is also a powerful antioxidant. It is probably the most controversial of all the vitamins.

We know that people do need some vitamin C because without 10 milligrams a day, a person would get scurvy. In years past, before the effects of vitamin C were known, whole armies were decimated by scurvy. It is estimated that more than 10,000 seamen died in the early days of exploration because they didn't have enough of this vitamin. However, once fresh citrus fruits were added to their diets, scurvy ceased to be a problem.

Vitamin C is made from glucose, a simple sugar found in ordinary table sugar. In order to turn the glucose into vitamin C, a special liver enzyme is required. Humans do not have that enzyme in their systems, so they must take in vitamin C from an outside source, such as oranges. Most other animals do have the ability to convert sugar into this necessary vitamin.

Most of the research relating to vitamin C has dealt with whether or not it can cure or prevent the common cold. Since there are at least 113 distinct viruses known to be able to cause a cold, it is unlikely that any one vitamin could work to limit all the viruses. However, it does seem to have some positive effects in protecting against colds. This might be due to the effects of collagen building or its role in building the immune system. There is some evidence that vitamin C might reduce mechanical damage to the lower limbs of runners by increasing the strength of the connective tissues through collagen formation.

The many studies relating vitamin C and colds have been inconclusive. If vitamin C helps to prevent colds, it is most likely to be the strengthening of the immune system before the viruses were encountered.

Smokers might require more vitamin C than the rest of us. This might not seem surprising in light of the earlier discussion of the protective effects of vitamin C as an antioxidant. It has been shown that smokers have lower blood levels of vitamin C than do nonsmokers, and smokers with a vitamin C deficiency have a greater chance of developing certain oral mucosal lesions than do others in the population

Vitamin D is seldom found to be deficient in the average diet. Not only can it be part of the diet, but it is also made by the action of sunlight on cholesterol near the skin. Just two to three 15-minute periods in the sun per week should produce sufficient vitamin D.

Vitamin E, like vitamin C, has many advocates who claim unproven benefits from its use. For example, vitamin E might be able to help cells live longer. This does not mean that vitamin E will slow the aging process, but it might indicate that the vitamin can be a shield against certain environmental stresses, such as smog, radiation, and other pollutants. This is because of its antioxidant properties. When cells treated with vitamin E were exposed to such environmental stresses, only 30 percent of the cells stopped reproducing compared to 90 percent of the untreated cells.

Another one of the major effects claimed for vitamin E is that it helps the hearts of humans and has been beneficial in the treatment of animal heart problems. This was first reported at the 1972 American Heart Association meeting. Some research now indicates that effective vitamin E supplementation might reduce heart attacks by as much as 40 percent. The lower rate of heart disease among those with high vitamin E levels was documented by the World Health Organization, which found that a low level of vitamin E was the most important predictor of heart disease. Sixty-two percent of those dying had such low levels. Heart pain (angina) and cancers also seem to be reduced by adequate intake of vitamin E. One factor that might be responsible is that vitamin E somehow blocks some of the clotting action of vitamin K, so it reduces the blood's tendency to clot.

A recent study indicates another aspect of this desirable type of supplementation. Mortality from coronary heart disease in 50- to 54-year-old men was found to be four times higher in Lithuania than in Sweden. Most risk factors were similar between the men in the two countries. The major difference seemed to be in the antioxidant intakes, particularly vitamin E. The Lithuanians were much lower. This corresponds with a study in England that showed that vitamin E supplements of from 400 to 800 IUs daily reduced the death rate from heart attacks by 47 percent.[3]

Vitamin E is a strong antioxidant that also acts as an anticoagulant. That is, it reduces the blood's ability to clot, so it reduces the risk of a coronary thrombus, a primary cause of heart attack, and brain embolisms, a primary cause of strokes. Like the other antioxidants, it reduces the risk of some cancers, of cataracts in the lenses of the eyes and it increases immunity to other diseases. In those who exercise, vitamin E also seems to reduce injuries to the small muscle fibers and might be important in preventing such conditions as shin splints.

Reports in the *British Medical Journal*[4] indicate that 2000 units of vitamin E delayed both the onset of Alzheimer's disease and the time of death. In the Cambridge Heart Antioxidant Study, 400 to 800 units of vitamin E daily considerably reduced the death rate from heart disease. Vitamin E is measured in either international units (solid form foods) or milligrams (if in oils). They are roughly equivalent measures. The minimum daily requirement is only 10 IUs (international units).

Vitamin K is necessary for two of the 14 steps necessary for the blood to clot. It is found in many foods, and in most people, it is produced in the intestines by bacteria.

MINERALS

Minerals are usually structural components of the body, but they sometimes participate in certain body processes. The body uses many minerals — phosphorus, calcium and magnesium for strong teeth and bones; zinc for growth; chromium for carbohydrate metabolism; and copper and iron for hemoglobin production in the blood.

Iron is used primarily in developing hemoglobin, which carries the oxygen in the red blood cells. Women need more iron than men until they go through menopause (18 milligrams a day), at which time their iron requirements drop to that of men (10 milligrams a day). The average amount of iron lost by menstruation is about 0.4 to 0.5 milligrams per day for sedentary women but is more than doubled for active women. When this is added to the 0.8 mg used or lost in normal daily living, about 1.3 to 2 mg per day should be enough. The problem is that, as with other vitamins and minerals, the amount that can be absorbed from the diet (its bioavailability) is much less than that which is consumed. The great majority of women would have enough iron if they could absorb 2.8 mg of iron daily. But to actually absorb 2.8 mg, most women would need to take in much more, from 15 to 50 mg per day.[5] While meat and foods rich in vitamin C aid in the absorption of iron, other foods, such as spinach, and drugs, such as antacids, can inhibit the uptake.

Iron deficiency, common in women athletes, might impair athletic performance and should be corrected with supplementation. If an athlete is exercising hard enough for the body to produce more hemoglobin and more red blood cells, but there isn't enough iron to make the hemoglobin, the blood cells can't be manufactured and the endurance of the athlete will be limited in this essential component of endurance.

Some athletes are anemic, either not having enough red blood cells or not having enough hemoglobin (the oxygen-carrying element in the red blood cells). The most common finding in athletes is a dilutional pseudoanemia that is caused by a plasma volume expansion rather than an actual blood loss. It is not a pathological state and normalizes after stopping training for three to five days. Blood-cell loss can occur in a number of ways, including menstruation, pregnancy, lactation, the continued injury to a body part (such as the foot strike in running), through small losses in the sweat and through losses through injury or illness, such as to the gastrointestinal tract or the genitourinary tract.[6] A number of studies have concluded that female runners lose iron into their intestinal tracts. The various studies show between eight and 85 percent of female runners lose iron this way. Also, two percent of marathoners and triathletes show visible blood in their feces after races.[7] But the main cause is insufficient iron in the diet.

Magnesium is the eighth most abundant element on the earth's surface. It seems to help activate enzymes essential to energy transfer. It is crucial for effective contraction of the muscles. Exercise depletes this element, so supplementation might be called for. When it is not present in sufficient amounts, twitching, tremors and undue anxiety might develop.

Calcium is primarily responsible for the building of strong bones and teeth. For this reason, it seems obvious that a diet that is chronically low in calcium would have a negative effect on one's bone strength. The result of this is brittle and porous bones as one gets older, a condition known as osteoporosis. This is diagnosed when the bone density shows a loss of 40 percent of the necessary calcium. It happens quite often in older people, especially women who have gone through menopause or have had their ovaries removed, as estrogen seems to serve a protective function against bone loss.

The inclusion of adequate calcium (which might be higher than the current Recommended Daily Allowance) in teenage and young adult years can aid in the development of peak bone mass, which can help prevent osteoporosis later on in life. Another contributing factor to osteoporosis is the imbalance of phosphorus to calcium in the typical diet. Calcium and phosphorous work together. They should be consumed on a one-to-one ratio. However, the average diet is much higher in phosphorus than calcium, leading to a leeching of calcium from the bones to make up for this imbalance.

Calcium is also necessary for strong teeth, nerve transmissions, blood clotting and muscle contractions. Without enough calcium, muscle cramps often result. Skipping milk, with its necessary calcium, might be the cause of menstrual cramping for some girls. The uterus is a muscle, and muscles need both sodium and calcium for proper contractile functioning. In the

Unifed States, 1300 mg per day are recommended for girls nine to 18. For women 19 to 51, it drops to 1000 mg.

Lack of calcium is also a major factor in the female athlete triad (see page 213). The loss of bone calcium (osteoporosis) might be reduced or reversed by taking calcium supplements. Calcitonin, a nasal spray, has been found to be effective in replacing lost calcium in the bones. This is particularly true for the lumbar spine area.[8]

Fluoride deficiency might be a primary nutritional deficiency in the Western world. It is a major preventer of cavities in the teeth. Fluoride helps build stronger bones and teeth.

Potassium is a chief mineral in cell growth. A deficiency can cause impaired nerve and muscle functions, ranging from paralysis to minor weakness, loss of appetite, nausea, depression, apathy, drowsiness, confusion, heart failure and even death. It is often low in female diets.

It helps to regulate the acid base balance of the blood and to regulate blood pressure. Studies have shown an increase in blood pressure when sodium intake is high. Such studies have also shown blood pressure is decreased when the potassium intake is increased. A one-to-one ratio of sodium to potassium is considered good. Most people are much higher than desirable in sodium intake and lower than desirable in potassium intake.

Sodium, along with potassium, helps to maintain the body's water balance. But too much can raise blood pressure levels because too much water is retained. Since it is the major mineral ingredient in sweat, it occasionally needs to be increased in very hot weather or when the athlete perspires too much.

Trace minerals are those that are found in very small amounts. Nearly every element found in the body is essential, but the trace minerals are required in such small amounts and are generally abundantly found in the diet, so there is little reason for dietary deficiency. Usually foods high in calcium and iron are high in the necessary trace minerals, which are involved in developing our antioxidant defense mechanisms. A few of the trace minerals are:

- *Copper*, which helps in the production of red blood cells. It also helps in the metabolism of glucose (sugar), with the release of energy, in the formation of fats in the nerve walls and in the formation of connective tissues. Deficiency of copper is very rare.
- *Manganese*, which is used in fat and carbohydrate metabolism, pancreas development, prevention of bone defects, muscle contraction and many other functions. It has not yet been observed as a human deficiency.
- *Zinc*, an ingredient in insulin and used in carbohydrate metabo-

lism. It is necessary for the normal growth of general organs, the prevention of anemia and the growth of all tissues. It also helps in wound healing. Zinc in excess of the recommended daily amount interferes with copper absorption and decreases the level of HDL cholesterol (the good cholesterol) in the blood.

- *Chromium*, which helps to regulate blood sugar and to metabolize fats and carbohydrates. It is also an antioxidant.

- *Selenium*, a mineral that is part of an essential enzyme (glutathione peroxidase), which protects a naturally occurring antioxidant (glutathione). It works with vitamins C, E and beta carotene. As vitamin E, it might reduce micro-injuries to the small muscle fibers. It might also reduce the risk of digestive cancers, especially of the stomach and esophagus. In fact, it seems to be protective against all cancers. It is found in greater abundance in North American soils than in European soils. Therefore, it is found more often in both plants and animals raised in America.[9] Side effects of an excess of selenium can include hair loss, digestive problems (vomiting, diarrhea, nausea), irritability, nerve cell problems and fatigue.

PHYTOCHEMICALS

Phyto (Greek for plant) chemicals include thousands of chemical compounds that are found in plants. Some of these are vitamins, but many have no known effect on us; however, more and more are being found to be highly beneficial. In the past, the phytonutrients found in fruits and vegetables were classified as vitamins. Flavonoids were known as vitamin P, cabbage factors (glucosinolates and indoles) were called vitamin U and ubiquinone was vitamin Q. Tocopherol somehow stayed on the list as vitamin E. The vitamin designation was dropped for the other nutrients because specific deficiency symptoms could not be established, and *vita* means life, so if the compound could not be found to be absolutely essential for life, it was dropped as a vitamin but is now classified as a phytochemical.

Various phytochemicals have been found to reduce the chance of cancers developing, reduce the chance of heart attack, reduce blood pressure, reduce the problems of menopause and increase immunity factors. Few of these have been reduced to pill form, such as vitamin pills, so they must be consumed in fruits and vegetables daily. It is suggested that each of us consume at least five servings of raw fruits or vegetables daily. Since many of the phytochemicals are heat sensitive, cooking can destroy some or all of the active ingredients.

We are a long way from developing highly effective phytochemical supplements, because there are so many elements and they might be de-

FOODS WITH ANTICANCER-ACTING PHYTOCHEMICALS
Highly effective: garlic, carrots, celery, soybeans, cilantro, cabbage, parsley, ginger, parsnips, licorice *Moderately effective*: onions, flax, citrus fruits, broccoli, cauliflower, brussels sprouts, tomatoes, peppers, brown rice, tumeric, whole wheat *Somewhat effective*: oats, oregano, barley, basil, cantalope, berries, mint.
(Adapted from; Clark, K. "Phytochemicals protect against cancer." *ACSM Health and Fitness Journal.* May/June 1998. P. 35)

stroyed in the processing. Garlic pills, for example, are available. However, for those that have been deodorized, some of the active ingredients have been removed. They were in the chemicals that gave the garlic its aroma.

Several types of phytochemicals are being studied

Plant sterols are somewhat similar to the animal sterol cholesterol but are unsaturated. These plant sterols compete for the same sites and thereby lower the blood cholesterol levels, often by 10 percent. Soy is a good source for such sterols. Most green and yellow vegetables, and particularly their seeds, contain essential sterols.

Phenols have the ability to block specific enzymes that cause inflammation. They also modify the prostaglandin pathways and thereby protect platelets from clumping, reducing the risk of blood clots. Blue, blue-red and violet colorations seen in berries, grapes and purple eggplant are due to their phenolic content.

Flavonoids is the name for a large group of compounds. They are found primarily in tea, citrus fruits, onions, soy and red wine. Some can be irritating, but others seem to reduce heart attack risk. For example, the phenolic substances in red wine inhibit oxidation of human LDL (the harmful low-density cholesterols). The biologic activities of flavonoids include action against allergies, inflammation, free radicals, liver toxins, blood clotting, ulcers, viruses and cancer tumors.

Phytoestrogens among the flavonoids and other phytochemicals can occupy the body's estrogen receptors and act like estrogen. Soy, found commonly in Oriental diets, is believed to be responsible for reducing many of the symptoms of menopause. When soy is added to the diets of post-menopausal women, symptoms such as hot flashes are reduced or disappear.[10]

Terpenes, such as those found in green foods, soy products and grains, comprise one of the largest classes of phytonutrients. The most intensely studied terpenes are carotenoids, as evidenced by the many recent studies on beta carotene. Only a few of the carotenoids have the antioxidant properties of beta carotene. These substances are found in bright yellow, orange and red plant pigments found in fruits and vegetables such as tomatoes, parsley, oranges, pink grapefruit and spinach.

Limonoids are a subclass of terpenes which are found in citrus fruit peels. They appear to protect lung tissue and aid in detoxifying harmful chemicals in the liver.

Coenzyme Q10 (ubiquinone) is another phytochemical and an antioxidant. It has been linked to DNA-related problems in both the nerves and the muscles.[11] It also works with both vitamin C and vitamin E in a number of actions in which all three are utilized together.[12]

As often happens, the research of the local scientists can influence the acceptance of the substance. While Q10 has been studied in the United States, Dr. Cooper does not recommend it as a daily antioxidant. On the other hand, the work of Jan Karlsson and others in Sweden makes Q10 a favorite among the Nordic peoples. The Swedish National Food Administration recommends two to 20 mg per day. Jan Karlsson recommends 50 to 100 mg per day, with elite athletes taking in 100 to 300 mg per day.[13]

SUPPLEMENTING VITAMINS AND MINERALS

Buying vitamin pills should be determined by what you need. Some people need more of a vitamin than others do. If you are on a weight-reducing diet, it is a good idea to take a multivitamin and mineral supplement as it is difficult to get all the vitamins and minerals you need while on a diet. Some studies indicate that runners do not need more than the recommended daily amounts of vitamins. The problem is that many people don't get the recommended daily amounts of each vitamin or mineral. And it now seems that none of us gets enough of the antioxidants that protect us from the damage done by the free oxygen radicals produced in our bodies. Those of us who live in air-polluted environments or those of us who exercise have a greater than normal need for antioxidants.

Don't buy every supplement you hear about. Wait for the scientific evidence. There are a number of supplements that have been suggested, but research does not indicate that the benefits will outweigh the negatives — or there is no evidence that they work. So, for now, save your money on bicarbonate, citrate, phosphate, ginseng, bee pollen, royal jelly, chromium, carnitine, coenzyme Q10, or medium chain triglycerides. Q10 does act as an antioxidant but does not have the power of vitamins C or E.

If there is a question about your dietary intake of nutrients, particularly vitamins and minerals, consult a metabolic disease specialist (a medical doctor specializing in nutrition and its related effects) or a sports dietitian.

America's most famous fitness guru, Dr. Ken Cooper, the doctor who started the aerobics revolution, now says that we should supplement our diets with certain vitamins and minerals, particularly the antioxidants. He disagrees with those who advise us to get all of our vitamins and minerals from our diet. Cooper says that it can't really be done. In fact, we need more of some nutrients than we could possibly take in through a normal diet.[14] He recommends: 25,000 units of beta carotene, 1000 mg of vitamin C, 400 mg of vitamin E (specifically d-alpha tocopherol — the natural form of vitamin E), 400 mg of folacin and coenzyme Q10. His message is: "You can age fast or age slow. It's up to you." Endurance athletes benefit from higher doses of antioxidants. Cooper suggests that anyone exercising more than five hours weekly should double the recommended dosage to combat excess free radical byproducts.

Dr. Cooper considers supplementation of the mineral selenium optional as long as you are getting 50 to 100 mg a day. Natural sources include 3.5 ounces of tuna (115 mg of selenium), a half-ounce of tortilla chips (120 mg of selenium), 3.5 ounces of lasagna noodles (96 mg) or spaghetti (65 mg). So, it is quite easy to get this mineral in a normal diet. However, fruits and vegetables are quite low in selenium. Meats, grains, and beans, on the other hand, are generally high.

The Alliance for Aging Research (AAR), based on 200 clinical studies, recommends that people at high risk for cancer, especially asbestos workers and smokers, should not take any beta carotene supplements. For others interested in health promotion and disease prevention, the group recommends the following ranges of supplements (in an aging population):

- Vitamin C: 250 to 1000 mg daily
- Vitamin E: 100 to 400 I.U.s daily
- Beta carotene: 17,000 to 50,000 I.U.s (10 to 30 mg) daily[15]

Dr. Dean Ornish's Preventive Medicine Research Institute (PMRI) conducts pioneering research on lifestyle (diet, exercise, stress management, and group support) and heart disease. PMRI research director Larry Scherwitz, Ph.D., says that if a three-day nutritional analysis reveals program participants are not obtaining adequate antioxidant levels in the diet, a range of supplementation is recommended — one to three grams vitamin C; 100 to 400 I.U.s of dry vitamin E daily; and 10,000 to 25,000 IUs of beta carotene.

Those who would like to get vitamins through food sources can get 1000 mg of vitamin C by eating 13 to 17 oranges or 44 tomatoes a day. Fifteen oranges will add 1100 calories to your diet, while the 40 tomatoes will add 950 calories to your daily intake. To get the 400 mg of vitamin E each day, as the recommended alpha-tocopherol, consume 50 tablespoons of Mazola margarine (50,000 calories), 400 cups of spaghetti (79,000 calories), 260 tablespoons of peanut butter (24,000 calories), 8,000 potatoes (700,000 calories), 300 cups of instant oat cereal (43,500 calories), 6½ pounds of potato chips (16,000 calories) or 32 pounds of canned tuna in oil (31,000 calories). Since 3500 calories will put on one pound of body weight for the average person, you will gain between five and 10 pounds a day if you want to get 400 units of vitamin E through *natural* sources. And the chemical in the pill is the same chemical found in the oats or the tuna.

Melatonin is a naturally occurring substance in the body. It tends to be reduced as we age. It is often taken by older people as an aid for sleeping and by travelers crossing several time zones who might be subject to jet lag. It was discovered to be a direct free radical scavenger less than 10 years ago. Besides its ability to directly neutralize a number of free radicals and reactive oxygen and nitrogen species, it stimulates several antioxidative enzymes that increase its efficiency as an antioxidant. In terms of direct free radical scavenging, melatonin interacts with the highly toxic hydroxyl radical. It has been widely used as a protective agent against a wide variety of processes and agents that damage tissues via free radical mechanisms.[16] There is not much evidence to suggest that runners need vitamin supplementation for increased running efficiency, assuming that all of the recommended amounts of vitamins are ingested each day. Since most diets leave something to be desired, a basic complete supplement is often suggested. However, there is some evidence that the B complex vitamins and vitamin C might help the body to acclimatize to heat, and vitamins C and E, as antioxidants, are often recommended when one's training volume is high.

It is also essential to refuel after exercise or competition. Carbohydrates must be ingested to bring the muscle glycogen back to normal and proteins will be needed to give the body the building blocks it needs to produce its natural antioxidants and to repair or regenerate muscle tissue.

Notes

1. Karlsson, J. "Advances in nutrition for high intensity training." Presentation at the World Congress on Sports Medicine, Orlando, Fl. June 3, 1998.

2. Brown, K.M., P.C. Morrice, G.G. Duthrie. "Erythrocyte vitamin E and plasma ascorbate concentrations in relation to erythrocyte peroxidation in smokers and non-smokers: dose response to vita-

min E supplementation. *American Journal of Clinical Nutrition.* 65 (1997): 496-502.

3. Kristenson et al. *British Medical Jour.* March 1997, 314 p. 7081

4. Pahor, M and Applegate WB "Recent advances: geriatric medicine." *British Medical Journal* 315:7115 (1997): 1071-1074.

5. International Nutritional Anemia Consultative Group. "Iron deficiency in women." Nutrition Foundation, Washington, D.C. 1981. Cited in Grandjean, A.C., J.S. Ruud, K.J. Reimers. "Nutrition" *Women in Sport* (Drinkwater, B. ed) Blackwell Science, Oxford, UK. 2000, 124.

6. Shaskey, D.J., G.A. Green. "Sports haematology." *Sports Medicine* 29:1 (2000): 27-38.

7. Harris, S.S. "Exercise related anemia" In *Women and Sport.* (Drinkwater, B. ed) Blackwell Scientific, Oxford, UK, 2000, 315.

8. Drinkwater, B. "Osteoporosis." Presentation at the World Congress of Sports Medicine, Orlando, FL, June 2, 1998.

9. Rayman, M.P. "Selenium: time to act." *British Medical Journal* 314:387 (1997). Editorial.

10. Zava, D.T. and G. Duwe. "Estrogenic and antiproliferative properties of genistein and other flavenoids in human breast cancer cells." *Nutrition and Cancer* 27:1 (1997): 31-40.

11. Karlsson, J. *Antioxidents and Exercise.* Champaign, IL: Human Kinetics. 1997, p. 63; Halliwell, B. and M. Gutterudge. "Oxygen free radicals and iron in relation to biology and medicine: Some problems and concepts." *Arch. Biochem.Biophys.* 246 (2986):501-514; Alessio, H.M. et al. "Evidence that DNA damage and repair cycle activity increases following a marathon race," *Medical Science in Sport and Exercise,* 22:751 (1990); Alesio, H.M. "Exercise-induced oxidative stress,"*Med. Sci. Sports Exerc.* 25 (1993): 218-224.

12. Karlsson, J. "Advances in Nutrition for High- Training." Presentation at the World Congress of Sports Medicine, Orlando, FL, June 3, 1998.

13. Karlsson, J. *Antioxidents and Exercise.* Champaign, IL: Human Kinetics. 1997, p. 105.

14. Keynote address at the American Alliance for Health, Physical Education, Recreation and Dance Annual Convention, Portland, Oregon, March 30, 1995; also, Cooper, Ken. *Antioxidant Revolution,* Thomas Nelson Publishers: Atlanta, GA. 1994.

15. "To take antioxidant pills or not? The debate heats up." *Tufts Nutrition Letter.* 12:3 (1994): 3.

16. Reiter, R.J., D. Tan, C. Osuna, Gitto "Actions of Melatonin in the Reduction of Oxidative Stress. a review." *J Biomed Sci.* 7:6 (2000): 444-458.

INFORMATION ON VITAMINS AND MINERALS

Vitamin	Solubility	RDA Recommended (Minimum) Daily Allowance	Functions	Deficiencies and Excesses	Sources
A	Fat soluble stored in body	*Men:* 5000 units (R=-retinol equivalents) *Women:* 4000 units (800 RE) *Toxic level:* 10,000 to 50,000 units (2000 to 10,000 RE), if from animal sources	1. Formation of body tissue 2. Development of mucous secretions in nose, mouth, digestive tract, organs (which slow bacterial entry 3. Development of visual purple in the retina of the eye, which allows one to see in the dark 4. Produces the enamel-producing cells of the teeth 5. Assists normal growth 6. Estrogen synthesis 7. Sperm production	Deficiences can cause night blindness, damaged intestinal tract, damaged reproductive tract, scaly skin, poor bones, dry mucous membranes and, in children, poor enamel in the teeth. Toxic symptoms (of Retinol): may mimic brain tumor (increased pressure inside the skull), weight loss, irritability, loss of appetite, severe headaches, vomiting, itching, menstrual irregularities, diarrhea, fatigue, skin lesions, bone and joint pains, loss of hair, liver and spleen enlargement and insomnia. In children, overdose can stunt growth.	Butter and margarine. Whole milk Liver Fish Fortified nonfat milk Fish liver oils Egg yolks

Vitamin	Solubility	RDA Recommended (Minimum) Daily Allowance	Functions	Deficiencies and Excesses	Sources
Beta-carotene	Fat soluble stored in body	As antioxidant, 25,000 to 50,000 units (15 to 30 mg)	1. Precursor to vitamin A 2. Antioxidant 3. Reduces cancer risk 4. Reduces heart disease	Deficiency: Increased free oxygen radical activity. Excess: may yellow the skin.	Carrots Broccoli Dark Green or orange fruits or vegetables
B$_1$ (Thiamin)	Water soluble	1.5 mg (men) 1.2 mg (women)	1. Metabolizes carbohydrates 2. Resulting glucose (sugar) nourishes muscles and nerves 3. Aids nerve functioning	Deficiencies can cause: mental depression, moodiness, quarrelsome-ness and uncooperativeness, fatigue, irritability, lack of appetite, muscle cramps, constipa-tion, nerve pains (due to degeneration of myelin sheath which covers the nerve), weakness and feeling of heaviness in the legs, beriberi (a disease in which the muscles atrophy and become paralysed)	Liver Pork Yeast Organ meats Whole grains Bread Wheat germ Peanuts Milk Eggs Soya beans
B$_2$ Riboflavin	Water soluble	1.8 mg (men) 1.4 mg (women)	1. Effects rate of growth and metabolic rate since it is necessary for the cell's use of protein, fat, and carboydrate	Deficiences can cause burning and itching eyes, blurred and dim vision, eyes sensitive to light, inflammation of the lips and tongue, lesions at the edges of the mouth,	Eggs Liver and other organs Yeast Milk Whole grains Bread

Vitamin	Solubility	RDA Recommended (Minimum) Daily Allowance	Functions	Deficiencies and Excesses	Sources
B$_2$ Riboflavin (cont.)			2. Growth 3. Adrenal cortex activity 4. Red blood cell formation	digestive disturbances, greasy, scaly skin, personality problems.	Wheat germ Green leafy vegetables
B$_3$ niacin or nicotinic acid	Water soluble Limited storage in body	20 mg (men) 15 mg (women)	1. Similar to riboflavin in metabolizing foods (especially sugars) 2. Maintain normal skin conditions 3. Aids in functioning of the gastrointestinal tract	Deficiencies can cause dermatitis, fatigue, sore mouth (tongue), diarrhea, vomiting, nervous disturbances, mental depression, anorexia, weight loss, headache, backache, mental confusion, irritability, hallucinations, delusions of persecution, pellagra. Large doses can be toxic because it dilates blood vessels. Can cause skin flushing, dizziness, head throbbing, also dryness of skin, itching, brown skin pigmentation, decreased glucose tolerance and perhaps a rise in uric acid in the blood.	Yeast Liver Wheat bran Peanuts Beans
Pantothenic acid	Water soluble Little storage in body	4-7 mg	1. Carbohydrate, fat and protein metabolism 2. Synthesis of cholesterol and steroid hormones 3. Aids in choline metabolism	Almost never deficient in human diets. Various animals studies have shown different results from deficiency: rough skin, diarrhea, anemia, possible coma,	Liver Organ meats Yeast Wheat bran Legumes Cereals

Vitamin	Solubility	RDA Recommended (Minimum) Daily Allowance	Functions	Deficiencies and Excesses	Sources
Pan-tothenic acid (cont.)			4. Aids the functioning of the adrenal cortex 5. Aids in choline metabolism	convulsions, hair loss and many other symptoms. But they have not been shown in humans	
Biotin	Water soluble	0-3 mg	Metabolism of amino acids, fatty acids and carbohydrates	Deficiencies are extremely rare. Raw egg whites, which combine with the biotin in the intestines and make it unavailable and some antibiotics (which kill the biotin-producing organisms in the intestines) could cause a deficiency. Deficiency would be marked by dry, scaly skin, gray pallor (skin color), slight anemia, muscular pains, weakness, depression and loss of appetite.	Manufac-tured in the intestines Also found in Liver, Yeast, Kidney, Egg yolks
B_6 pyridoxine	Water soluble	2.0 mg (men) 2.0 mg (women)	1. Catalyst in protein, fat and carbohydrate metabolism. 2. Converts tryptophan to niacin 3. Assists in nervous system 4. Antibody production	Anemia, dizziness, nausea, vomiting, irritability, confusion, kidney stones, skin and mucous membrane problems. In infants: irritability, muscle twitching, convulsion. Excesses: impaired sensation in limbs. Unsteady gait.	Usually not necessary to supplement. Wheat germ Kidney Liver Ham Organ meats Legumes Peanuts

Vitamin	Solubility	RDA Recommended (Minimum) Daily Allowance	Functions	Deficiencies and Excesses	Sources
Folic acid (folacin)		0.2-0.4 mg	1. Aids in maturation of red and white blood cells 2. May assist in the synthesis of nucleic acids 3. DNA synthesis	Blood disorders, anemia, diarrhea. Deficiencies most likely to occur during pregnancy and lactation.	Yeast Liver Egg yolk Green leafy vegetables
B₁₂	Water soluble stored in the body	60 mg	1. Controls blood forming defects and nerve involvement in pernicious anemia 2. Involved in protein, fat, carbohydrates, nucleic acid and folic acid metabolism 3. Necessary to the normal functioning of cells, especially in the bone marrow, nervous system and intestinal tract	Sore tongue, amenorrhea, signs of degeneration of the spinal cord, anemia, heart and stomach trouble, headache and fatigue.	Liver organ meats Oysters Salmon Eggs Beef Milk
C (ascorbic acid)	Water soluble Little stored in the body	60 mg 10 mg per day prevents scurvy Recommended as antioxidant: 1-1.5g	1. Forms collagen intracellular cement, which strengthens cell walls, tooth dentine, cartilage, bones and connective tissue	Scurvy results from low vitamin C intake. Minor symptoms of vitamin C deficiency could be subcutaneous hemorrages and bleeding gums.	Citrus Fresh fruit Berries Broccoli Tomatoes Baked potatoes

Vitamin	Solubility	RDA Recommended (Minimum) Daily Allowance	Functions	Deficiencies and Excesses	Sources
C (ascorbic acid) cont.			2. Aids in the absorption of iron 3. Aids in formation of red blood cells in the bone marrow 4. Aids in the metabolism of some amino acids (phenylalanine and tyrosine) 5. May be involved in the synthesis of steroid hormones from cholesterol 6. Any body stress may deplete the vitamin C in the tissues, which may increase shock or bacterial infections 7. Antioxidant	Excess of vitamin C can result in kidney stones and diarrhea, destruction of B_{12} acidosis	Green leafy vegetables Turnips
D	Stored in liver Fat soluble	400 units (10 mgm) Toxic level: 1000 to 1500 units (25 to 38 mgm)	1. Assists in the development of bones and teeth by aiding calcium to harden 2. Facilitates the absorption of calcium and phosphorus, lack of which can cause muscular cramping	Deficiencies: rickets, osteomalacia (women who have frequent pregnancies and poor diets). Teeth may be more susceptible to caries (cavities). Cramping in muscles if there is low level of calcium or phosphorus in the blood. Soft bones, bowed legs, poor posture.	Exposure to ultraviolent light (sunlight) can give minimum daily require- ments by changing one type

Vitamin	Solubility	RDA Recommended (Minimum) Daily Allowance	Functions	Deficiencies and Excesses	Sources
D (cont.)			3. Neuromuscular activity	Toxic symptoms: fatigue, weight loss, nausea, vomiting, weakness, headache, kidney damage, kidney stones, hardening of the soft tissue of the heart, blood vessels, lungs, stomach and kidneys. Increases cholesterol level of blood. Makes bones more fragile. High levels in developing fetuses and young children may cause mental retardation or blood vessel malformation (especially a blockage in the aorta).	of cholesterol to Vitamin D, Milk Fish liver oils Egg yolk Butter Whole milk Nonfat milk (with D) Margarines (with D added)
E (toco- pherol)	Fat soluble not stored in body	10 units 10 mg TE (tocopherol equivalents) As an antioxidant: 400 units (TE) 600 units (if over 50 years, 2500 if heavy exerciser)	1. It is thought to stabilize mem- branes 2. May be helpful in stabilizing Vitamin A 3. May be neccesary in diets high in polyunsatu- rated fats. 4. Aids in synthe- sizing red blood cells. 5. Antioxidant	No known defiency symptoms in human adults. Some premature infants apparently do not immedi- ately develop the ability to absorb the vitamin.	Synthe- sized in the intestines. Human milk (cow's milk poor) Margarine oil, salad dressing Cereal germ Green leafy vegetables

Vitamin/ Mineral	Solubility	RDA Recommended (Minimum) Daily Allowance	Functions	Deficiencies and Excesses	Sources
K	Fat soluble	Men: 80 mgm Women: 63 mgm	Helps in the production of prothrombin (blood clotting agent)	Antibiotics taken orally (which could kill the synthesizing bacteria) or diarrhea (which could flush out the bacteria) could possibly cause a deficiency. Newborn infants, especially premature babies, often suffer from a deficiency. This may cause excessive bleeding. Toxic symptoms in infants: jaundice, mild anemia	Synthesized by intestinal bacteria Green leafy vegetables Cabbage Cauliflower Smaller amounts in tomatoes, egg yolk and whole milk

MINERALS

Calcium		1200 mg	Development of strong bones and teeth. Helps muscles contract and relax normally, Utilization of iron. Normal blood clotting. Maintenance of body neutrality. Normal action of heart muscle.	Rickets, porous bones, bowed legs, stunted growth, slow clotting of blood, poor tooth formation, tetany	Milk, cheese, mustard, turnip greens, clams, oyster, broccoli, cauliflower, cabbage, molasses, nuts. Small amount in egg, carrot, celery, orange, grapefruit, figs, and bread made with milk

Mineral	RDA Recommended (Minimum) Daily Allowance	Functions	Deficiencies and Excesses	Sources
Flourine	1.5-4 mg	Resistance to dental caries. Deposition of bone calcium. May be involved in iron absorption.	Deficiencies: weak teeth and bones, anemia, impaired growth. At levels of 1.5 to 4 parts per million teeth will be strong but may be mottled. At levels over 6 ppm, teeth and bones may be deformed.	Water supply containing 1ppm Small amounts found in many foods
Iodine	0.15 mg	Constituent of thyroxine, which is a regulator of metabolism. Synthesis of vitamin A	Enlarged thyroid gland. Low metabolic rate, stunted growth retarded, mental growth	Iodized salt Sea foods Food grown in nongoitrous regions
Iron	*Men*: 10 mg *Women*: 15-18 mg	Constituent of hemoglobin, which carries oxygen to the tissues. Colagen synthesis, antibody production	Nutritional anemia, pallor, weight loss, fatigue, weakness, retarded growth	Red meats, especially liver, green vegetables, yellow fruits, prunes, raisins, legumes, whole grain and enriched cereals, molasses, egg yolk, potatoes, oysters

Mineral	RDA Recommended (Minimum) Daily Allowance	Functions	Deficiencies and Excesses	Sources
Magnesium	*Men:* 350-400 mg *Women:* 280-300 mg	Activates various enzymes. Assists in breakdown of phosphates and glucose r neces- sary for muscle contraction. Regulates body temperature. Assists in synthesizing protein. Tooth enamel stability.	Failure to grow, pallor, weakness, irritability of nerves and muscles, irregular heartbeat, heart and kidney damage, convulsions and seizures, delirium, depressions	Soya flour, whole wheat, oatmeal, peas, brown rice, whole corn, beans, nuts, soybeans, spinach, clams
Phosphorus	800–1200 mg	Development of bones and teeth. Multiplication of cells. Activation of some enzymes and vitamins. Mainte- nance of body neutrality. Partici- pates in carbohy- drate metabolism ADP/ATP synthesis acid/base balance DNA/RNA synthesis	Rickets, porous bones, bowed legs, stunted growth, poor tooth formation. Excesses of phosphorus may have same effect on the bones as deficient calcium (osteoporosis porous bones)	Milk, cheese, meat, egg yolk, fish, nuts, whole grain cereals, legumes, soya flour, whole wheat, oatmeal, peas, brown rice, whole corn, beans

Mineral	RDA Recommended (Minimum) Daily Allowance	Functions	Deficiencies and Excesses	Sources
Potassium	2.5 grams	Acid-base balance. Carbohydrate metabolism. Conduction of nerve impulses. Contraction of nerve impulses. Contraction of muscle fibers. May assist in lowering blood pressure (if consumed in equal proportions as sodium).	Apathy, muscular weakness, poor gastrointestinal tone, respiratory muscle failure, tachycardia (irregular heartbeat), cardiac arrest (heart stops beating)	Soya beans, cantaloupe, sweet potatoes, avocado, raisins, banana, halibut, sole, baked beans, molasses, ham, mushroom, beef, white potatoes, tomatoes, kale, radishes, prune juice, nuts and seeds, wheat germ, green leafy vegetables, cocoa, vegetable juices, cream of tartar, prunes, figs, apricots, oranges, grapefruit

Mineral	RDA Recommended (Minimum) Daily Allowance	Functions	Deficiencies and Excesses	Sources
Selenium	*Men:* 70 mgm *Women:* 55 mgm As an antioxidant: up to 100 for heavy exercisers	Antioxidant: may reduce risk of stomach and esophogeal cancers	Toxic level: nausea, hair loss, diarrhea, irritability	Organ meats, meats, milk, fruits
Sodium	1–2 grams (1/5 to 2/5 teaspoon)	Constraint of extra-cellular fluid. Maintenance of body neutrality. Osmotic pressure. Muscle and nerve irritability. Acid/base balance.	Muscle cramps, weakness, headache, nausea, anorexia, vascular collapse Excess may raise blood pressure.	Sodium chloride (table salt) Sodium bicarbonate (baking soda) Monosodium glutamate The greatest portion of sodium is provided by table salt and salt used in cooking. Foods high in sodium include: dried beef, ham, canned, corned beef, bacon, wheat, breads, salted crackers, flaked breakfast cereals, olives, cheese, butter, margarine, sausage, dried fish, canned vegetables, shellfish and salt water fish, raw celery, egg white

Mineral	RDA Recommended (Minimum) Daily Allowance	Functions	Deficiencies and Excesses	Sources
Zinc	*Men:* 15 mg *Women:* 12 mg	Metabolism, formation of nucleic acid enzyme formation collagen production, fetal development, enhanced appetite and taste	Impaired growth, sexual development, skin problems	Beef, chicken, fish, beans, whole wheat, cashew nuts

17
EATING FOR FITNESS AND WEIGHT CONTROL

Sensible eating for fitness requires an understanding of the basic principles of nutrition that were discussed in the previous two chapters. The nutrients must appear in the diet in proper quantities, and the calories must be the amount necessary in order to maintain your desired weight while on your fitness exercise program. If your desired weight is not maintained, then overweight or obesity might develop. Diseases associated with being overweight — diabetes, high blood pressure, heart disease — can also begin.

There are other factors that the sensible eater must understand. Caloric needs change according to climate and the amount of activity in which you participate. It is obvious that hot weather or endurance exercise necessitates a greater intake of fluids due to the loss of water through perspiration. In hot weather, if you don't exercise, there is a lesser need for calories because your body does not need to burn as many calories to maintain its normal temperature of 98.6 degrees.

A person using a great many calories, such as an endurance athlete, needs more carbohydrates. It is a myth that athletes need a great deal more protein than nonathletes. While the caloric needs might nearly double for the athlete who is expending a great deal of energy, the protein needs are increased only slightly, usually less than 30 percent. Another myth concerning athletes is that they require more vitamins and minerals than do others. Supplements given to athletes who are already consuming well-balanced diets have not been shown to improve performance. However, as noted in the last chapter, antioxidant supplements might reduce long-term body damage that comes with living — and exercising.

IMPORTANT CONSIDERATIONS IN SELECTING YOUR DIET

The U.S. Department of Agriculture has devised a suggested diet guide called the Food Guide Pyramid. Grain products form the base; next come fruits and vegetables; then meats and animal products. At the

top are some fats or sweets, if needed. Recommended servings in the six food groups are:

1. Grain products (breads, cereals, pastas): 6 to 11 servings per day
2. Vegetables: 3 to 5 servings per day
3. Fruits: 2 to 4 servings per day
4. High-protein meats and meat substitutes (meat, poultry, fish, beans, nuts, eggs): 2 to 3 servings per day
5. Milk products: 2 servings for adults; 3 for children
6. Extra calories, if needed: fats and/or sweets

Grain products provide the carbohydrates that are needed for quick energy. A serving size would be one slice of bread, an ounce of dry cereal or a half-cup of cooked cereal, pasta, or rice. The grains are rich in B vitamins, some minerals and fiber. Whole grains are the best sources of fibers. Refining grains or polishing rice reduce the fiber, the mineral content and the B vitamins. This occurs in white and wheat bread (not whole wheat), pastas, pastries and white rice. The flour is often refortified with three of the B complex vitamins but seldom with the other essential nutrients.

If you are concerned with reducing your cholesterol level and reducing your chances of heart disease, reducing your chances of developing gall stones or having a softer stool in your bowel movement, eat more of the soluble fibers (oat bran cereals, whole grain bread with oats, carrots, potatoes, apples and citrus juices which contain the pulp of the fruit, or rice bran). If your concern is reducing your risk of intestinal cancers, appendicitis and diverticulosis, eat more of the insoluble fibers (whole wheat breads and cereals, corn cereals, prunes, beans, peas, nuts, most vegetables and polished rice).

Vegetables are rich in fibers, beta carotene, some vitamins,and minerals. Among the most nutritious vegetables are broccoli, carrots, peas, peppers and sweet potatoes. If you are trying to lose weight, many vegetables are high in water and in fibers but low in calories. Among these are all greens (lettuce, cabbage, celery) as well as cauliflower. Actually, most vegetables are quite low in calories. A serving size would be a half-cup of raw or cooked vegetables or a cup of raw leafy vegetables. You need three to five servings daily.

Fruits are generally high in vitamin C and fiber. They are also relatively low in calories. A serving size would be one-fourth cup of dried fruit, one-half cup of cooked fruit, three-fourths cup of fruit juice, a whole piece of fruit or a wedge of a melon. You should have two to four servings daily.

Protein sources such as meats, eggs, nuts and beans, are also high in minerals and vitamins B6 and B12. A serving would be 2.5 ounces of cooked meat, poultry or fish, two egg whites, four tablespoons of peanut butter, or 1¼ cups of cooked beans. You need two to three servings a day. A McDonald's Quarter Pounder would give you two servings. The hidden eggs in cakes and cookies would also count. The best meat products to eat are fish (because of the omega-3 oils that reduce blood clotting), egg whites and poultry without the skin.

Red meat not only has a relatively low quality of protein (ranked after egg white, milk, fish, poultry, and organ meats), but it is linked to both heart disease and cancers (2.5 times the risk for colon cancer). It also carries a large amount of fat, even if the fat on the outside is trimmed off. There is also a great deal of cholesterol in the meat and fat of most animals. Taking the skin off of poultry significantly reduces the amount of fat and cholesterol that will be consumed. Poultry products carry much of their fat next to the skin.

Of the flesh proteins, fish is the best. It has a higher quality of protein than meat or poultry, and it contains the helpful omega-3 oils. Fish are able to convert the polyunsaturated linolenic fatty acid from plants that they eat into omega-3 oils. These work to prevent heart disease by reducing cholesterol and by making the blood less likely to clot in the arteries. They do this by interfering with the production of the prostaglandin thromboxane that increases blood clotting.

Milk and milk products (cheeses, yogurt, ice cream) are high in calcium and protein as well as some minerals (potassium and zinc) and riboflavin. Whole milk and low-fat milk and milk products contain a large amount of saturated fats. Skim (nonfat) milk and its products do not contain fat. A serving would be one cup of milk or yogurt, 1.5 ounces of cheese, two cups of cottage cheese, 1.5 cups of ice cream, or one cup of pudding or custard. Adults need two servings daily; children need three.

Fats and sweets are noted at the top of the pyramid of foods. They are there only if a person needs extra calories. Fats over the recommended maximum of 30 percent of one's diet can be quite harmful, particularly in causing cancers and hardened arteries. Most researchers suggest a level of 10 to 20 percent of the diet in fats, most in the form of monounsaturated and polyunsaturated fatty acids. The official government maximum is 30 percent of total fats with no more than one-third in saturated and the rest in approximately equal levels of monounsaturated and polyunsaturated fats.

Sweets might assist in the development of tooth decay (cavities) but are not otherwise harmful if calories are not a problem for you. A runner or walker consuming 5000 calories in a day can probably eat candy bars and ice cream. The person attempting to control one's weight should avoid them.

In addition to merely consuming these foods, a concerned person would emphasize several cautions:

- Avoid milk fat by drinking nonfat milk and milk products; eating ice milk (three percent fat) or frozen desserts made without milk fat; and eating no- or low-fat cheeses. Half of the calories in whole milk come from the 3.5 percent of fat in the milk. Low-fat milk has reduced the fat calories by 40 percent. When low-fat milk is advertised as 98 percent fat free, it is not that much better than whole milk, which is 96.5 percent fat free. Milk is mostly water. The fats in milk are highly saturated, the worst kind of fat. Yet, the protein quality of milk is second only to egg whites.

- Egg yolk should be avoided because it contains a great deal of cholesterol. Eggs are second only to caviar (fish eggs) in cholesterol content. Egg yolks are the worst thing for most people to eat because of the high cholesterol and saturated fat content. Egg white, however, has the highest rating for protein quality, so it is one of the best things that can be eaten.

- Reduce salt, because it is related to high blood pressure, and sugars, because they give empty calories or calories without other nutrients such as vitamins or fibers.

- Reduce fats to between 10 and 20 percent of your calories. Normal salad dressings contain upward of 70 calories per tablespoon. If calories are a problem, use fat-free dressing or vinegar or lemon juice only. Rather than butter or margarine, buy a good, tasty whole-grain bread and eat it without grease. If you must use a spread on your bread, use olive oil or olive oil and garlic, as is served in many Italian restaurants. If calories are not a concern and you like sweets, use a jelly or jam.

- Never fry foods in oil; use a nonstick pan. If you must have oil, however, use canola (rapeseed), olive or safflower oil. Avoid all fried foods, including potato chips. Fried foods not only add calories and saturated fats, but they increase the chances for intestinal cancers, as do all fats.

BEVERAGES

Beverages make up a large part of our diet. We often don't think too much about the kinds of liquids we drink. The most nutritious drinks have been rated by the Center for Science in the Public Interest. They were rated according to the amount of fat and sugar (higher content = lower rating) and their amount of protein, vitamins, and minerals (higher content = higher rating). The results were that skim or nonfat milk was rated a +47, whole milk +38 (the lower rating was because of its fat content), orange juice +33, Hi-C +4, coffee 0, coffee with cream -1, coffee with sugar -12, Kool-Aid -55 and soft drinks -92.

Nonfat milk is the best beverage for most people. Children should have three to four cups each day. Adults should drink two cups. Our need for milk can also be satisfied by other dairy products. For example, two cups of milk are equivalent to three cups of cottage cheese or five large scoops of ice cream. (Of course, this choice might taste the best, but there are obvious drawbacks to eating five scoops of ice cream everyday!) In addition to its nutrient value as a developer of bones and organs, milk has been found to help people sleep. They not only go to sleep more quickly, they sleep longer and more soundly. This is because of the high content of the amino acid tryptophan, which makes serotonin, the neurotransmitter associated with relaxation and calming activity.

Coffee contains several ingredients that might be harmful to the body. There are stimulants such as caffeine and the xanthines. There are oils that seem to stimulate the secretion of excess acid in the stomach. And there are diuretics that eliminate water and some nutrients, such as calcium, from the body. Even two cups a day increases the risk of bone fractures.[1] A factor that might add to the risk of bone fractures is that people who drink more coffee usually drink little or no milk.

Caffeine is found in coffee, tea and cola drinks. Brewed coffee contains 100 to 150 milligrams of caffeine per cup (mg/cup), instant coffee about 90 mg/cup, tea between 45 and 75 mg/cup and cola drinks from 40 to 60 mg/cup. Decaffeinated coffee is virtually free of caffeine, as it contains only two to fiour milligrams per cup. The therapeutic dose of caffeine given to people who have overdosed on barbiturates is 43 milligrams. Yet, a cup of coffee contains up to 150 milligrams of caffeine!

While there are a number of negatives relative to caffeine, for a runner, there might be some positives. One of the reasons that caffeine is often used as an ergogenic energy producer is that it can break down the fat more quickly. An excess of caffeine in the system is enough to disqualify you for an Olympic medal because excess caffeine is on the International Olympic Committee's list of banned drugs.

Caffeine is a central nervous system stimulant. It elevates blood pressure and constricts the blood vessels. Both of these might contribute to the development of high blood pressure. It has also been reported that excess caffeine in coffee, tea and cola drinks can produce the same symptoms found in someone suffering from psychological anxiety. These symptoms include nervousness, irritability, occasional muscle twitching, sensory disturbances, diarrhea, insomnia, irregular heartbeat, a drop in blood pressure and, occasionally, failures of the blood circulation system.

Coffee is an irritant. The oils in coffee irritate the lining of the stomach and the upper intestines. People who drink two or more cups of coffee per day increase their chances of getting ulcers by 72 percent over noncoffee drinkers. Decaffeinated coffee is no more soothing to the ulcer patient than the regular blend because both types increase the acid secretions in the stomach. Since an ulcer patient's acid secretion is not as high when caffeine alone is ingested (when compared to the acid levels after the ingestion of decaffeinated coffee), some other ingredient in coffee is thought to be responsible for these increasing stomach acid levels.

Tea is not as irritating as coffee, but it does contain some caffeine and tannic acid, which can irritate the stomach. If you drink large amounts of tea, you should take it either with milk to neutralize the acid or add ice to dilute it. Green tea, the type drunk commonly in the Orient, contains polyphenols, which appear to be antioxidants that might reduce cancer incidence. The black tea commonly consumed in Europe and America, has less of these protective substances.[2] Not much is known about the effects of herbal teas.

There are seven calories in a gram of alcohol. These calories contain no nutritional elements, but they do contribute to your total caloric intake. Since alcoholic drinks are surprisingly high in calories, they greatly contribute to overweight problems of many individuals. People who drink alcoholic beverages and eat a balanced diet will probably consume too many calories. If they drink but cut down on eating, they might not develop a weight problem, but they will probably develop nutritional deficiencies that can result in severe illness. Alcohol is also a central nervous system depressant, which causes a decrease in metabolism.

In addition to the normal dangers of alcohol in creating alcoholism and destroying brain cells, there are other considerations in drinking.

Beer or ale, because of their carbonation, have the effect of neutralizing stomach acid. This might increase the acids secreted by the stomach, which could cause ulcers. Gin contains juniper berries and other substances that are stomach and intestinal irritants.

FOOD ADDITIVES

Sugar is a negative for most people. In fact, it is probably the most harmful additive to the foods that we in the United States eat. We average about 125 pounds of sugar per person per year. This gives us a lot of excess calories that, if we don't use them for energy, will be stored as fat. As discussed previously, if we exceed our desired weight and become obese, it will lead to increased health risks. If your exercise program is heavy, such as training for competitive running or walking, sugars in your recovery drinks might be essential. However, it is best to take in the maltodextrins found in most sports drinks rather than the sucrose found in most candy and cakes.

Salt can be a dangerous additive to foods because people react differently to salt. Most people do not consider adding salt to their food a health risk, but when you look at populations as a whole, it seems obvious that the higher the salt intake, the greater the frequency of high blood pressure. If you are exercising in hot weather, it should not be a problem and might, in fact, be necessary.

Since many manufacturers add salt to enhance the taste, sodium is often high. While the desired intake is between one and two grams (1000 and 2000 milligrams), the average intake in America is five grams.[3] Negative effects of high sodium intake can be combated by ingesting high levels of potassium. However, the desired recommended daily allowance for potassium, 2.5 grams, is not met by average Americans, who consume only 0.8 to 1.5 grams daily.[4] Most of our foods follow this same pattern — too high in sodium and too low in potassium.

Preservatives added to foods give a longer storage life and prevent disease-causing germs from multiplying. Most are harmless. Some protect against intestinal cancers. Some, such as the nitrates in hot dogs, are cancer-producing. However, botulism, which nitrates are preventing, is far more of a danger than is the infinitesimal amount in the wiener.

Vitamins and minerals have been added to food for years. In 1973, the Food and Drug Administration suggested that more iron be added to enrich flour after it found that iron is often low in our diets. Vitamins A and D are added to skim milk to make it nonfat milk — milk that has all of the nutrients of whole milk but without the fat. Vitamins A and D are fat soluble and stayed in the fat when the fat was removed to make the skim milk.

VEGETARIANISM

When vegetarians are careful about their dietary intakes, they might prove to be healthier than nonvegetarians. One study compared healthy vegetarians to nonvegetarians and found that healthy vegetarians had lower blood sugar and cholesterol levels than did their closely matched nonvegetarian counterparts. Their greatest problem is in getting enough vitamin B12, which is found primarily in meat.

SMART SHOPPING

Shopping for low-fat foods requires a sharp eye. If you are looking for a low-fat food, look at the total grams of fat, multiply by nine, then divide that by the total number of calories in the food. (For example, three grams of fat times nine calories in a gram of fat equals 27 total calories from fat. If the food had a total of 270 calories in it, then the percentage of fat calories = 10 percent.) If the food has one of the new food labels on it, all you need to do is divide the number of fat calories by the total number of calories for the food. This is how you calculate the approximate percentage of fat calories per serving. You want to keep your total percentage of fat below 30 percent every day to decrease your risk of developing heart disease. Ten to 20 percent fat is better than the suggested maximum of 30 percent.

Many foods, particularly low-fat liquids such as salad dressings without oil, have replaced the thickness of the oil with some gums. Guar, locust bean and xanthine gums are soluble fibers, so they help to remove cholesterol from the intestines. You get a double advantage: no fat and some cholesterol removal substances.

The ingredients in the food must be listed according to their content in the product. The higher on the list of ingredients, the more of that item that is present in the food. So, if the product lists wheat flour first, there is no problem. However, if it lists eggs or hydrogenated oils second, the food might be too high in fat. If you are on the lookout for sodium, remember to look for where salt is listed.

EATING AND OVEREATING

Obviously, people eat to nourish their bodies, but in America, many people eat as a means of reducing stress. We might not be satiated in our work, at school or in our relationships, but we can be satiated with food. Filling our stomachs can make us feel that, in at least one part of our lives, we are totally satisfied. When eating to relieve stress we will probably take in more calories than we need for living, but what's worse is that stress eating is often done with junk foods.

Gaining weight is a desire for some people. When one focuses on weight gain, she is focused on increasing her lean body weight. This means that she wants to increase her weight by increasing muscle mass, not fat. To gain weight in muscle, the best method is to do resistance-type exercise, such as weight training. Second, you must ensure that you are eating enough protein in order to give your body the building blocks that it needs to make more muscle. It is not necessary to eat excessive protein, as this dietary practice brings with it its own set of health risks.

Being overweight is a more common concern than is being under-weight. While some people are overweight, some are obese. Thirty-five percent of women are 20 percent overweight.[5] Of people who are obese, one in 20 is so because of a genetic factor or a problem in physical mal-functioning, such as an underactive thyroid gland or a problem with the hypothalamus, or one of the other centers of the brain that deals with whether or not we feel full or hungry. There are medical procedures that can help these people. In cases where the metabolism is slowed, such as by an underactive thyroid gland, doctors can administer the proper hor-mone to increase metabolism back into what is considered a normal range.

Another cause of obesity is thought to be the number of fat cells in a person's body. This is known as the set-point theory. It is thought that the more fat cells one has, the more one is driven to eat to maintain these fat cells. The number of fat cells one has is generally set after puberty. After this, it is the size of the fat cells that changes to accommodate fluc-tuations in weight. Fat cells in an obese person might be three times as large as those in a lean person. Dieting might make the fat cells reduce in size, but not in number. The thinner cells just sit around waiting to be fed.

For others, obesity can be caused by extreme overeating. However, according to the Harvard University Nutrition Department, most people who are too fat are that way because they lack exercise, not because they overeat. Overeating, coupled with a lack of exercise, is a sure way of becoming obese.

Since it is the amount of fat that a person carries on his/her body that is the true culprit of disease, it is preferable to refer to being overfat as a health risk rather than being overweight. Many body builders might be overweight when compared to the height and weight charts commonly used to measure health risks by insurance companies, but they are not overfat.

There are several ways to determine if you are overfat. The most com-mon method is to look at yourself in a mirror. If you look fat, you might be fat. Another way is to pinch the fat you carry just below the skin. If you can pinch an inch, you are probably carrying too much fat. Profes-sionals often use skin calipers to measure the amount of fat people carry in four to seven designated spots on the body or they use underwater weighing or bioelectrical impedance.

Once your body-fat percentage is determined, you can then find out what a healthy weight would be for you. Women are healthy if they fall between 18 and 25 percent body fat, while men are usually considered healthy if their body fat is in the range of 10 to 15 percent. Men are considered overfat if their body fat is more than 20 percent, while women are overfat if their body fat is over 30 percent. Women require more fat than do men due to the menstrual cycle. If a woman falls below 12 percent body fat, she might become amenorrheic (lose her regular menstrual cycle). Some women become amenorrheic at a 14 to 15 percent body fat level.

Another concern for your health is where you store your fat. Those who store their fat in the abdomen, thereby resembling an apple shape, are at a higher risk for developing heart disease than those who store their fat in the hips and thighs, thereby resembling a pear shape. So, if two women have the same percentage of body fat but different shapes, the one who is apple-shaped is at a greater risk than the pear. As you might have noticed, most men tend to be apple-shaped, while most women tend to be pear-shaped. Thus, most women are at a lower risk than most men, simply because of where they store their fat.

Should you lose weight? Before you decide, first determine whether you are overweight due to being overfat. From a health point of view, it is your proportion of fat and lean body mass that is most important.

HOW TO LOSE WEIGHT

The wisest approach to losing weight would be to find out why you are overweight. If it is genetic, perhaps medical help is needed. If you eat because of stresses, you should find another method to relieve the stresses, such as exercise or relaxation techniques or, if you must have something in your mouth, try gum or a low-calorie food. If your problem is a lack of exercise, start an effective exercise program. If you consume too many calories, change your diet.

Don't even start a weight-loss program if you are not willing to make lifestyle changes for the rest of your life. The great majority of dieters refuse to make such a commitment, which is why 40 percent of women and 25 percent of men are on a diet at any one time and that the average American goes on 2.3 diets a year and why 95 percent of dieters have regained all of their lost weight within five years. If you honestly want to lose weight, you need a real commitment to both your diet and your exercise program. The rewards are certainly worth it in terms of health, longevity and self-esteem.

In all likelihood, adopting the habits of effective exercise, with a low-fat and low-alcohol eating pattern, will drop the pounds off. Losing weight just for the sake of being thinner seldom works for very long. Consequently, you will have to determine whether you honestly want a healthier lifestyle or you just want to look better for the summer. A pattern of continually gaining and losing is frustrating and probably not worth the effort. However, a true lifestyle change of healthy eating and effective exercise will pay many mental, physical and social dividends.

We must recognize that the fat we wear comes primarily from the fat we eat. Because of the efficiency of conversion to the sugar glucose, carbohydrates are used first for energy in the body. To convert carbohydrates to fat requires about 23 percent of the energy potential in the carbohydrate to be used to make the conversion to fat. Protein, if not used, will normally be converted into sugars and will be the second source of available energy. But fat that you have consumed uses only three percent of its food value to convert it to body fat.

So, 25 grams of carbohydrate, which should yield 100 calories (at four calories a gram), is reduced by the 23 percent of the calories that were used to convert the carbohydrate into body fat. But fats consumed in your food are different. Eleven grams of fat (at nine calories per gram) is 99 calories, but it only takes three percent of those calories to convert it all to body fat. Consequently, 96 calories of the fat consumed, if not used for energy, can be deposited as 10.75 grams of body fat. However, a similar number of calories of carbohydrate, if not used for energy, will become only 8.5 grams of body fat.

As a runner, unless you are anorexic, you should normally have enough fat on your body. The average runner has enough fat in the body to supply the energy to run 40 back-to-back marathons at a 2:40 pace. Still, the fat is more slowly converted into energy than is carbohydrate, which resynthesizes the adenosine triphosphate (ATP) more quickly.

COMBINING EXERCISE WITH FOOD RESTRICTION FOR WEIGHT LOSS

To lose one pound of fat per week, you must have a net deficit of 500 calories per day. This is because one pound of fat contains 3500 calories. You might choose to achieve this solely by decreasing your food intake by 500 calories per day. However, if this is your approach, be warned: your metabolism will slowly decrease over time to accommodate for the decrease in food energy, thereby making it harder and harder for you to continue to lose fat.

You should also choose to increase your activity level to burn off 500 calories a day. Keep in mind that it takes a great deal of energy to achieve this goal, and it can be dangerous for you to embark on such a strenuous exercise program if you are currently not exercising. Therefore, it is best to combine calorie reduction with exercise to achieve your goal. Aerobic exercise, such as walking or running, will keep your metabolism up as you lose the fat, and you won't have to restrict your calories to such an extreme because you will be burning off energy each time you exercise.

We now know that calories are used both during and after exercise. The longer and more vigorous the exercise, the longer one's metabolism is increased, and the more hours after the exercise is completed that the calorie expenditure will be increased over normal. While this increase in calories burned after one has finished exercising is not a large amount, it is still an increase over one's resting metabolism. And a calorie burned is a calorie burned!

To give you an idea of equivalents of food, walking and running, below are some comparisons to show approximately how long a 120-pound woman would need to walk or run to burn off the listed food.

From the chart, it is clear that 20 minutes of walking isn't going to burn off the Big Mac, chocolate shake and fries. On the other hand, 20

Food	Kilocalories	Fitness Walking	Running (9 minute mile)	(5.20 min mile)
Sugar-sweetened cappucino, one cookie, slice cracked wheat bread	60	10 min.	6 min.	4 min.
Coca Cola (12 oz) or beer (12 oz) Ounce of peanuts	154	25 min.	13 min.	10 min.
Mars or Milky Way candy bar, High-quality ice cream (1/2 cup), McDonalds hamburger	251	41 min.	22 min.	16 min.
McDonald's shake or medium fries	320	53 min.	28 min.	20 min.
Big Mac	560	1 hr., 33 min.	50 min.	35 min.

minutes of walking each day will burn off about a pound a month if you don't increase your food intake from what you now eat.

Some people think that exercising will make them eat more. A quarter mile to a mile of jogging will have no measurable effect on the total reduction of calories. But by exercising just before a meal, you can dull your appetite and decrease your desire for more calories.

CARBOHYDRATE LOADING FOR COMPETITION

Carbohydrate loading is often effective when a competitive distance run takes more than 60 minutes. The original concept of carbohydrate loading was suggested in the 1960s by the renowned Swedish exercise physiologist Per Åstrand. He suggested a strenuous workout a week before the competition to exhaust the muscle glycogen (sugars), then a three-day reduced carbohydrate intake period to reduce glycogen storage even more. For the last three days, the training is greatly reduced and the carbohydrate consumption is significantly increased. This is done to overstock the glycogen-starved muscles with glycogen for extra energy during the race. The strategy does increase carbohydrate storage, but it might come at a price. The hard training session within a week of the competition might overfatigue the runner or, worse, an injury could be inflicted.

During the 1980s, an equally effective, but less dangerous, approach to carbo loading was developed. Both the hard training session and the three-day reduced carbohydrate diet were eliminated. The only requirement is to cut carbohydrate intake to 50 percent of calories from seven to four days before the race, then, for the last three days increase carbohydrates in the diet to 70 percent. You might want to supplement the high-carbohydrate diet with additional high-carbohydrate drinks.

In either type of carbo loading, when the body accumulates more glycogen, it does it in combination with water. This makes the body heavier and can slow the running economy during the first part of the race. As the glycogen is used, the body becomes lighter and the second part of the race should be faster.

EATING DISORDERS

Anorexia nervosa is starvation by choice. This is a disease primarily seen in young women. It afflicts at least one in 100 women and nearly one in 1000 males. In this disease, the person goes on a diet and refuses to stop, no matter how thin she gets. About one out of 10 people who have this affliction end up starving themselves to death. The disease has a psychological basis, but its physical effects are very real. Medical care, usually hospitalization, is generally required.

After the anorexic begins the severe dieting routine, symptoms of starvation might set in leading to a number of physical problems. Abnormal thyroid, adrenal, and growth hormone functions are not uncommon. The heart muscle becomes weakened. Amenorrhea occurs due to the low percentage of body fat. Blood pressure might drop. Anemia is common due to the lack of protein and iron ingested. The peristalsis of the intestines might slow and the lining of the intestines might atrophy. The pancreas often becomes unable to secrete many of its enzymes. Body temperature might drop. The skin might become dry and there can be an increase of body hair in the body's attempt to keep itself warm. The worst effect of the disease is death.

Because dieting is such a common occurrence in our society, anorexia is often difficult to diagnose until one has entered the advanced stages of the disease. However, other symptoms, such as moodiness, being withdrawn, obsessing about food but not being seen eating it, and constant food preparation might be observed by those close to the anorexic. Once diagnosed, there are a number of medical and psychological therapies that can be effective.

Bulimia or *bulimia nervosa* is more common than anorexia. It is typified by the person restricting calorie intake during the day and bingeing on high-fat, high-calorie foods at least twice a week. Following the binge, the person will then purge in her attempt to rid the body of the excess calories just consumed. Purging techniques include vomiting, laxatives, fasting, and excessive exercise. Some experts do not consider the behavior bulimic until it has persisted for about three months with two or more binges per week during that time. Estimates based on various surveys of college students and others indicate that between five and 20 percent of women might be bulimic. It is also more common among men than is anorexia.

Bulimia, like anorexia, stems from a psychological problem. However, there might also be a link to physical abnormalities in some cases. The neurotransmitters serotonin and norepinephrine seem to be involved as does the hormone cholecystokinin, which is secreted by the hypothalamus and makes a person feel that enough food has been eaten.

Physical symptoms that might be seen depend on the type of purging technique used. The bulimic who induces vomiting can have scars on the back of the knuckles, mouth sores, gingivitis, tooth decay, a swollen esophagus, and chronic bad breath. The bulimic who uses laxatives can cause irreparable damage to the intestines due to constant diarrhea. All bulimics run the risk of throwing off their electrolytes (minerals involved in muscle contractions) due to constant dehydration suffered. It is this imbalance of electrolytes that can cause the bulimic to have abnormal heart rhythms and can induce a heart attack.

THE FEMALE ATHLETE TRIAD

Female athletes have often developed problems called the *female athletic triad.*[5]

This triad is a combination of eating disorders, osteoporosis and amenorrhea. The combination of hard training, for competitive athletes or dancers, and the desire to keep weight reduced often results in inadequate nutrition. This is sometimes achieved by bulimic methods. The result is weight that is too low, a loss of calcium from the bones and a lack of healthy menstruation.

These problems are most likely to occur in activities in which low weight is an advantage, such as dancing, distance running, figure skating and gymnastics. It is more prevalent among athletes in individual sports than in team sports. Males, with the exception of competitive wrestlers, do not often experience the need to eat less.

If you have the time and patience to analyze your basic nutrients, it is highly suggested that you purchase the latest edition of *Food Values of Portions Commonly Used* by Dr. Jean Pennington. It is published by Lippincott Williams and Wilkins. Now in its 17th edition (1998), it is an absolutely essential book for anyone who wants to evaluate her diet or parts of her diet. There are thousands of foods listed, each analyzed according to the number of calories, amount of protein, amount of carbohydrates, amount of fiber, percentage of fat (broken down into saturated, monounsaturated and polyunsaturated fats, the amount of cholesterol, the amount of vitamins (A, B1, B2, B6, folacin, niacin, B12, pantothenic acid and C) and minerals (sodium, calcium, manganese, magnesium, zinc, potassium, phosphorus, iron, and copper). In addition, there are lengthy lists of essential amino acid amounts in common proteins, alcohol content of various drinks, caffeine content of foods, high sugar-containing foods, vitamin E-containing foods and a number of other such lists. For nearly 40 years, the author has used and recommended this book to anyone interested in nutrition. There is no other like it. The cost today is in the $40 range and is well worth the price.

Notes

1. Barrett-Connor, E. "Caffeine and bone fractures," *Journal of American Medical Assn.* Jan. 26, 1994.
2. *Univ. of California Wellness Letter*, January (1992): 1-2.
3. Briggs, George M. and Doris Calloway. *Bogert's Nutrition and Physical Fitness*. Philadelphia: W. B. Saunders. 1979: 246.
4. Ibid, 248.
5. *Harvard Women's Health Watch*, Nov. (1994): 4.

6. Nattiv, Aurelia, Drinkwater, Barbara, et al. "The female athletic triad," *Clinics in Sports Medicine: The Athletic Woman*. W.B. Saunders: Philadelphia. 13:2, (1994): 405-418.

SELF-TESTS

Do I have a healthy diet?

Place the number that best describes your answer to each question:
3—Almost always; 2—Sometimes; 1—Almost never

_____ 1. Do you eat three or more pieces of fruit per day? (Fruit juice counts as one piece.)

_____ 2. Do you eat a minimum of three servings of vegetables each day, including a green leafy or orange vegetable?

_____ 3. Do you eat three or four milk (milk, cheese, yogurt) products per day?

_____ 4. Do you eat a minimum of six servings of grain products (breads, cereal, pasta) each day?

_____ 5. Do you eat breakfast?

_____ 6. Do you eat fish at least three times per week?

_____ 7. Do you avoid fried foods? (including potato chips and french fries)

_____ 8. Do you eat fast food two or fewer times per week?

_____ 9. Are the milk products you consume made from nonfat milk?

___ 10. Do you avoid high-sugar foods and highly refined carbohydrates? (such as sweet rolls, cookies, nondiet sodas, candy, etc.)

Score: 25-30: You are balancing your diet well.

18-24: Your diet can use improving.

10-17:Your diet is unhealthy.

Do I have bulimia?

Answer: never, sometimes, or often.

_____ 1. Is your life a series of constant diets?

_____ 2. Do you vomit or do you take laxatives or diuretics to control your weight?

_____ 3. Do you have alternate periods of eating binges and fasts to control your weight?

_____ 4. Does you weight fluctuate by as much as 10 pounds because of eating habits?

_____ 5 Have you ever had a food binge during which you ate a large amount of food in a short period of time?

_____ 6. If you binged, was it on high-calorie food such as ice cream, cookies, do-nuts or cake?

_____ 7. Have you ever stopped a binge by vomiting, sleep or by experiencing pain?

_____ 8. Do you think your eating habits vary from the average person's?

_____ 9. Are you out of control with your eating habits?

_____10. Are you close to being 100 pounds overweight because of your eating habits?

If you marked two or more of the above questions "often," you might have a serious eating disorder called bulimia. For help or more information, contact one of the following groups:

Anorexia Bulimia Treatment Education Center: (800) 33-ABTEC

Bulimia Anorexia Self-Help: (800) 227-4785

18

STRETCHING AND FLEXIBILITY

Flexibility exercises are done primarily to increase the range of motion in a joint; however, they also stretch connective tissue in the belly of the muscle and also stretch the muscle itself. Effective stretching can make your athletic movements easier and can reduce the risk of injuring yourself by overstretching muscles and tendons during your walking or running.

THE FUNCTION OF THE BODY'S CONNECTIVE TISSUES

When we stretch, we are affecting either the skeletal system or the muscular system or both. Both systems have connective tissues as essential elements. The body's connective tissues are made largely from a protein called collagen, the most common type of protein in the body. Collagen has two very important factors: it is very strong and it is highly resistant to stretching. One study showed that a force 10,000 times greater than the weight of a fiber of collagen would not change its length.[1]

There are five major types of collagen. The most common (type I) is found in both ligaments and tendons as well as in skin and bone. Ligaments are tissues that connect bones to bones. Tendons connect muscles to bones. But there are also elastic-like tissues in our ligaments and tendons — more so in the ligaments. Consequently, we have cells in our connective tissues that stretch quite well, while other cells resist stretching. It is the latter that is our concern in developing adequate flexibility.

The skeletal system is made up of 206 bones, each connected to adjacent bones by connective tissue called ligaments. Each joining of bones is a joint. Some joints are very mobile, such as the wrist or shoulder joints, which allow many types of motion. Other joints are immobile or nearly immobile, such as the joints where the ribs join the sternum (breastbone) or the joints of the fibula and tibia in the lower leg.

There are a number of types of joints in the body. Some merely work as hinges (knee) and some are ball-and-socket joints (hip and shoulder). Others slide one bone on another (wrist and ankle), while still others allow for rotation or other types of movement.

It is in these joints that your range of motion is determined. If your elbow joint is too loose or if there is an unusual shape at the end of the bones, the arm might be able to be bent backward past its normal limits. (This would be called hyperextension and is caused by an unusual laxity in the elbow joint.) If you have normally tight ligaments in the hip joint, which connects to the thigh bone (femur), but you wanted to be a sprinter who could take a long, efficient stride, you would need to stretch the ligaments in the back of the joint capsule to allow for such a movement. In fact, you would need stretched ligaments in both the front and the rear of your hip joint.

The average person will not want to stretch the ligaments much because it can weaken the basic structure of the joints. However, as opposed to tendons, ligaments are slightly more elastic, allowing greater movement of the joints. Some ligaments, especially some found in the neck and lower back, are quite elastic.

If you need to increase your range of motion in a specific joint, it might be desirable to stretch those ligaments. Also, there are occasional abnormalities of the joints that require some stretching in order to allow for a full range of motion. These situations should be diagnosed by medical specialists.

The muscular system contains a number of types of connective tissues. There are the tendons and the collagen sheaths, which encircle both the large muscles and the small muscle fibers within those muscles.

It is the function of the tendons to transmit all of the force generated by the muscle to the bone into which it connects. Obviously, if the tendon stretched every time there was tension on it, there could be no effective force transferred to the bone. It would be like trying to tow a car with a rubber band rather than with a chain. In fact, if a tendon is stretched more than four percent, it is likely to be injured.

In stretching exercises, you are generally concerned with stretching the collagen fibers in the muscular system. A lack of flexibility commonly appears when the connective tissues in the muscles, tendons, or ligaments shorten — something that happens when we age or are inactive. In the good old days of weightlifting and bodybuilding, it was quite common.

Muscle-bound was a term that was applied to bodybuilders or weightlifters who did not have adequate flexibility. We now know that muscles can never be bound. However, the connective tissue that surrounds the muscles, and the tendons that attach the muscles to the bones can be shortened and thereby reduce flexibility. The problem with the old-time body builders was that they did not do their exercises through a full range of motion. Consequently, the connective tissue in their biceps muscles was short — from biceps curls in which they did not straighten their arms as the weight was lowered. Also, the connective tissues in their chests were shortened due to bench presses in which they did not allow the bar to drop to the chest.

Fascia is a term applied to connective tissue that is not otherwise identifiable as ligaments, tendons or other common types of collagen. Fascia, which binds the muscle fibers and encases the muscle belly; fascia, which binds our organs and holds them in place; and fascia under the skin are a few examples of this type of tissue.

When a muscle contracts in order to move something, some of the muscle's power is used to overcome internal friction and tension. The fascia between the muscle fibers and around them are said to provide more than 40 percent of that internal resistance that the muscle encounters in developing its force. The joint capsule (the friction of one bone moving against another plus the tightness of the connective tissue in and around the joint) provides about 47 percent of the internal resistance. The muscle's tendon accounts for about 10 percent of the internal resistance and the skin adds another two percent to the total resistance. It is the force left over, after these internal frictions have been overcome, that will move your bones and create strength or power.

With these resistance factors in mind, if you are interested in efficiency of movement because you are a runner or competitive walker, stretching the connective tissues in the areas in which you need extra flexibility should be of value. Such stretching not only increases your range of motion but can also reduce your chances of injury due to making a movement that could overly stretch the connective tissue.

THE EFFECT OF HEAT AND COLD ON STRETCHING

Most studies indicate that connective tissues can be more effectively stretched if they are heated. So, a warm up or warm water might allow for greater stretching. In laboratories, ultrasound waves are often used to warm the tissues. Additionally, cooling the muscles in cool water after stretching can help to set the stretched condition. This cooling must be done before the stretch is relaxed.[2] But because the muscle should be heated deeply, the effect of applying warm compresses to the muscle might not always help, and the results might be similar to stretching a muscle that has not been warmed.[3] So, most of us are best served by walking, jogging or running for several minutes before we begin to stretch.

RANGE OF MOTION

In each of the above types of movement, your joints will exhibit greater or lesser amounts of movement ability. Your range of motion is the measure of flexibility for each joint or combination of joints. That range of motion is determined by the connective tissues (ligaments) that surround the joint as well as the tendons and the tension in the muscle fibers. When tension in the muscle is high, the muscle is said to be in a state of contracture. The contactures can generally be reduced by effective stretching exercises within a few weeks. Movement restriction caused by tight ligaments will generally take much longer than merely stretching the muscle tissues.

Some people are rightly concerned with increasing their range of motion. Most dancers need great flexibility. Many athletes also need flexibility beyond what is normally needed for day-to-day living. Hurdlers, divers, high jumpers, soccer kickers and sprinters are just a few of those who might need to increase their range of motion in order to be more effective in their chosen activities.

THE EFFECTS OF AGING ON CONNECTIVE TISSUES

Water makes up 60 to 70 percent of our connective tissues when we are young. As we age, our connective tissues become more brittle. By age 70, we have lost about 20 percent of the water content that was in the connective tissues when we were born, so our total water has been reduced to approximately 50 percent of the connective tissues. In addition, our collagen becomes thicker, so we become stiffer and less flexible. A more obvious illustration of this aging effect shows in our skin, where the loss of water in the collagen reduces the skin's ability to spring back, resulting in wrinkles.

We can reduce the aging of our connective tissues if we maintain an effective stretching program throughout our lives. But even those who have not been careful to maintain flexibility can undo much of the damage of inactivity by beginning to stretch in the ways described below.

BECOMING MORE FLEXIBLE

Flexibility comes from stretching the body's connective tissues: the tissue that holds one bone to another (ligaments), the tissue that holds muscles to bones (tendons) and the tissue that holds the individual muscle bundles together. If you are not flexible, you will not have a full range of motion for each joint. When you are too tight, you must use excess muscle power just to make a simple movement.

For example, if the connective tissue in the front of your hips is too tight, you won't be able to extend your leg as far backward when running. If the connective tissue in the front of the shoulders is too tight, you won't be able to swim as effectively. Also, if you are not sufficiently flexible, it is easier to sustain an injury such as a sprain (ligament damage)

TYPES OF STRETCHES
1. Static stretch occurs when you hold the position. 2. Ballistic stretch is a stretch done when moving. 3. Active stretch occurs when you supply the power for the stretching. 4. Passive stretch occurs when you are relaxed and another person, or a device, aids you in stretching.

or a strain (muscular or tendon damage).

Flexibility is quite simple to achieve. Most of us touched our toes every day during physical education classes in school, but we might have forgotten to continue the practice. You could probably easily touch your toes when you were 12. Can you do it now? The connective tissue tends to shorten if we do not keep it stretched, so most of us have lost some flexibility between the time we were in the eighth grade and now.

STRETCHING FOR FLEXIBILITY VERSUS STRETCHING FOR WARM-UP

There is no question that if we are not sufficiently flexible to do an activity, we must stretch effectively. There is also no question that as we age, there is some shrinking of connective tissue, which might cause us to have pain. Low back pain in older people is often caused by tightened fascia in the lower back. There is also no question that most of us think that we should stretch before every activity. We did it in our physical education classes and in most of our supervised sports activities. However, this pre-exercise stretching is now open to question. Research on stretching has not answered all, or even most, of our questions on whether to stretch, when to stretch or how to stretch (see Chapter 4). So, stretching as part of the warm up is not now recommended, but stretching after the workout when the muscles are warm is wise, if we need more flexibility.

FLEXIBILITY EXERCISES

Stretches should be held for 20 to 30 seconds in order to get the maximum benefits. If you find that you are particularly tight in one area, do the exercise several times a day.

The toe touch keeps your lower back and the back of your hips and thighs flexible. While most people do it standing, it is more effective to do

Toe touch

Thigh and groin stretch

it while sitting on the floor. When you are sitting and stretching forward, the muscles in the back of your torso and thighs relax so you can stretch farther. When you are standing, those same muscles remain somewhat tight because they are fighting the gravity that is allowing you to bend downward

Thigh and groin stretch. From a standing position, step forward with your left leg. Lean forward over your left leg while keeping your left foot flat on the floor. Push down with your right leg until you feel a good stretch in your thigh and groin area. You can put your hands on the ground for balance. Stretch for 30 seconds, then do it with the other leg.

The splits are a forward-backward stretch for the tissue at the front and the rear of the upper thighs. Becoming flexible in these areas makes it easier to do any long striding when running or sprinting. Put the right foot forward and the left back. Keep moving them farther and farther apart. Then put the left leg forward and the right back.

The groin stretch: While seated on the floor, put the soles of your feet together and pull them toward your hips with your hands. With your back straight, press your knees outward toward the floor. Do this for 30 seconds. This could be useful if you were running in the hills where there is more tension on the groin from the uneven terrain, with one leg often higher than the other in the stride.

Thigh rotation works to stretch the connective tissue that would prevent a full range of rotational motion. While sitting with your legs outstretched, turn your toes in as far as they will go for 15 to 30 seconds, then outward as far as they will go for 15 to 30 seconds.

Trunk twist: While sitting on the ground with your legs straight, flex your right leg and cross it over your left leg and put your right foot flat on the ground. Reach your left arm around your bent leg as if you were trying to touch your right hip. Place your right arm behind you as you slowly twist your head and neck until you are looking over your right shoulder. Hold for 30 seconds, then do the exercise to the other side. If you prefer to do it standing, spread your legs, reach your right arm up, then turn to the left as far as you can and hold. Then, reach your left arm up and turn to the right.

The shoulder and chest stretch is primarily for posture. It allows you to stretch the muscles that, if too tight, tend to give you a rounded-shoulder look. While standing or sitting, raise your arms to shoulder level, flex the elbow to about 90 degrees, then pull your elbows back as far as possible. You will feel the stretch in your upper shoulder and chest. This exercise not only stretches your chest,but also strengthens the muscles in the upper back, which will allow you to easily hold your shoulders in a more correct postural position.

Shoulder and chest stretch

The calf stretch might be the most important stretch for runners. It stretches the calf muscles (gastrocnemius and soleus), the Achilles' tendon and the tendons and ligaments under the foot that can be affected by plantar fasciitis. To do this stretch you can stand facing a wall but three or more feet away from it. While keeping your feet flat on the floor, lean into the wall until you feel the stretch in the heel cord and behind the knee. Since you do not want to overstretch the Achilles' tendon the knees should be slightly flexed during a calf-stretching exercise.

Tibialis anterior stretch can ready the muscles in your leg, which might be subject to shin splints, to be better prepared for running. While sitting, push down on the top of your foot until you feel the pull in the front of your leg about six inches below your knee.

POTENTIALLY DANGEROUS STRETCHES

While stretching certain joints and muscles is essential for some purposes, such as keeping mobility in an injured joint or increasing one's range of motion for an athletic event, there are times when a particular stretch might be harmful. If a stretch puts a harmful pressure on a joint or if a stretch is harmful to a particular person, obviously that stretch should be avoided. A number of stretches have been considered to be harmful, but often there are as many experts on one side of the issue as on the other. (See: Alter, M. *Science of Flexibility*. Champaign, IL: Human Kinetics, 1996, pp. 211-220 for comments of experts on some of the following exercises.) You sometimes read in books that research has shown that an exercise is harmful. But no research is quoted and neither is research that takes the opposite position. The questionable exercises nearly always are those that flex the knees more than 90 degrees or that flex or hyperextend the lumbar spine. Here are a few exercises that have been criticized:

- The deep knee bend is universally considered to be dangerous for the knee ligaments. Still, it is a basic position for Olympic-style weightlifters.

- The hurdler's stretch, done sitting with one leg stretched forward and the other fully flexed and next to the stretched leg with the foot next to the hip, is an exercise that puts too much stress on the knee, just as does the deep knee bend. When the nonstretched thigh is abducted to a 90-degree angle to the hip, the knee should not be in a compromising position; however, the extreme abducting stretch might not be necessary for most people. Of course, if you are a hurdler, it is a necessity.
- The standing toe touch is not as effective as the sitting toe touch, as was explained earlier in the chapter. An additional caution would be for those middle-aged or older who have back problems. The bending forward might put additional stress on the discs on the front side of the lower (lumbar) spine.
- Extreme hyperextension of the spine (a back bend) might excessively stretch the ligaments in the front of the spine and possibly cause unwanted pressure to the rear of some of the discs. Also, it stretches the connective tissues in the abdominal muscles — and we need all the help we can get to hold in our abdomens. The warning against severe hyperextension has been taken by some to ban any extension of the spine that passes the line of normal posture.
- The *plow exercise* is done with the back on the floor and the legs raised over the head with the toes touching the floor behind the head. This can put excessive stretch on the outside of the spine or the neck (cervical spine).

The questions to ask when considering a stretching exercise are: do I need the flexibility in that area of my body, and do I have a physical problem that could be made worse by stretching?

STRETCHING TO PREVENT INJURY OR TO AID IN RECOVERY

Overuse injuries are quite common in certain sports in which there is a long-term continuous strain on part of the body. Cyclists often have wrist problems, tennis players elbow problems and runners often have foot, thigh and leg problems. Stretching might reduce some of these problems.

Contractures are problems that often affect runners. They are caused by excess muscle tension in the hamstrings (back of thighs) and the calf muscles. In about half of the cases, this problem can be corrected with effective stretching of the affected muscle.

Prevention of running injuries and contractures can often be accomplished by the use of orthotics. These are shoe inserts that properly support the bones of the feet and often allow for an effective stretching of the ligaments and tendons, which can prevent problems such as shin splints (pain in the front of the shin), plantar fasciitis (pain under the heel and foot) and contractures.[4]

Lower back pain afflicts nearly seven million people. It is often a result of poor posture but can also be caused by muscle strain, mental stress, poor sleeping habits and other conditions. Often, it can be relieved or cured by the proper lower-back stretches recommended earlier in the chapter.

Hammer toes is a condition in which the toes curl under. If surgery isn't required, the toes can be stretched upward with the hands.

Plantar fasciitis is an inflammation of the tendons that extend forward from the heel bone under the foot. Stretching the toes, as above, and the Achilles' tendon, as described previously, are generally recommended for relieving the pain and preventing a reoccurrence. A cure often takes six months to a year and is aided by a proper orthotic shoe insert.

Shin splints can be relieved by pushing downward on the top of the foot in order to stretch the tissues in the front of the lower leg or tibia.

Notes:

1. Verzar, F. "Aging of Colagen." *Scientific American*, 208:4 (1963): 104-117.
2. Lentell, G. et al. "The use of thermal agents to influence the effectiveness of a low-load prolonged stretch." *Journal of Orthopedic and Sports Physiotherapy*. 16:5 (1992): 200-207.
3. Taylor, B.F. et al. "The effects of therapeutic application of heat or cold followed by a static stretch on hamstring muscle length." *Journal of Orthopedic and Sports Physical Therapy*. 21:5 (1995): 283-286.
4. D'Ambrosia R.D. "Orthotic devices in running injuries." *Clinical Sports Medicine* 4:4 (1985): 611-618.

19
DEVELOPING STRENGTH

Strength becomes more important when the desire to walk or run faster is important. Long-distance running requires more endurance; sprinting requires more strength.

Two major factors affect our ability to move effectively with strength: the number of muscle fibers contracting at one time and the efficiency of the lever (joint and muscle attachments). Every joint is a lever that varies in efficiency. The biceps muscle in the front of the upper arm works on a more efficient lever than does the calf muscle (gastrocnemius), which allows one to rise up on the toes. And levers also vary in efficiency from person to person. Those who have shorter bones generally have better lever actions than those with longer bones. Heavily muscled people generally have more efficient levers and more muscle fibers than do the tall, thin people. This is why you don't see tall, thin competitors in Olympic weightlifting events.

When we see a muscle bulge under our skin, we are seeing the outline of the muscle belly. That belly of the muscle is actually made up of millions of muscle cells and billions of working elements within each cell.

STRENGTH

There are four types of muscle contractions:
- *Concentric (isotonic)* or *dynamic*: exercises in which the muscle moves a joint through a certain range of motion. Pushing the body upward in a push-up or jumping up would be examples of concentric exercises.
- *Isometric* exercises: the muscle contracts but does not move the joint. Examples would be holding an object without moving it or standing in a doorway and pushing out on the door jamb.
- *Eccentric*: the muscle is lengthening rather than shortening during the exercise. An example would be lowering your body back to the floor during a push up or landing on the ground after jumping upward.

- *Plyometric*: a combination of eccentric then concentric contractions rapidly performed. An example would be landing from a jump, then rebounding into another jump. There is a great deal of research in the sport community on this stretch-shortening cycle.[1]

Depending on the kind of muscular action you require, your choice of exercise will vary. For example, if you are concerned about strength in the calf muscle, which absorbs the body's weight as the foot lands, then pushes the body forward at the end of the stride, you would want concentric, eccentric and plyometric types of exercise. Isometric exercises would not help much.

SPECIFICITY

Strength, in everyday terms, can mean of number of different measures of force. For example, power is the name we give to strength that is generated quickly — it is speed plus strength. If you want power, because you are a sprinter, a soccer player, a dancer or in another activity in which you want quick strength, you must exercise specifically for that.

If you were attempting to run faster, you could do leg exercises with heavy weights and it would probably help you a bit, but using an isokinetic machine that allowed you to move faster against resistance would be more effective. The isokinetic machines can allow for greater speed because they work against air pressure (Keiser) or mechanical braking systems (Nordicflex Gold).

Even the position of your body when you do the exercise affects its ability to exert the same kind of strength in another body position. For example, if you do biceps curls in an upright position (standing or sitting), that strength does not all transfer to doing the same curls when lying down. Even doing a bench press or doing a push up — nearly identical exercises — doesn't transfer the strength gained to the other exercise.[2]

USING MANUAL RESISTANCE FOR STRENGTH GAIN

While the ideal method of gaining strength is by the use of heavy resistance apparatus, such as barbells, dumbbells and weight machines, it is possible to gain strength by using your own body as resistance for the muscles. The following exercises do not require apparatus.

For the front of the chest (upper pectorals) and the back of the upper arms (triceps), do *push ups*. If you cannot do a regular push up, the resistance can be reduced by keeping your knees on the floor or by pushing away from a wall.

For the front of the upper arms (biceps), lie on the floor face up. Bend your legs while keeping your feet flat on the floor, lock your hands behind your thigh and pull your head and shoulders up to the knees. This exercise will also stretch the back muscles. Another exercise for the biceps is to use your hand to give you resistance while you flex the other arm.

For the muscles in your thighs, steady yourself by holding on to a table. Do a one-legged, half-knee bend. Do not let the upper leg go past the position at which it is parallel to the floor. Connective tissue in the knee might be damaged if you do a full knee bend. If you are not strong enough to do a one-legged knee bend, do the exercise with both legs. By doing the exercise with one leg rather than two, you double the amount of weight the leg muscles are forced to lift.

For your calf muscle, steady yourself by holding onto a table, then rise up on your toes. Do this one leg at a time.

If you can do the exercises more than 10 times, you need more resistance if they are to be an effective strength exercise. If you prefer muscular endurance because you are a distance runner or a walker, use many repetitions. Two-legged, rather than the one-legged, exercises will reduce your resistance, so you will be able to do many more repetitions.

RESISTANCE TRAINING FOR STRENGTH

The most common exercises done in gyms and weightlifting classes generally involve at least two muscle groups acting at the same time. For example, the bench press and the push up both use the upper chest muscles and the back of the upper arms. It is impossible to determine just how much each muscle group is working when these exercises are done.

For example, if two people do push ups, one might be doing 55 percent of the work with the chest muscles and 45 percent with the triceps. Another person might be doing far more of the pushing with the triceps than with the chest muscles.

For general strength conditioning, exercises that use two muscle groups are fine. However, if you are a person who wants to develop each muscle to its greatest strength, it would be best to isolate the muscles you desire to develop. As a runner or walker, you would probably want to isolate your calf, thigh, gluteal and hamstring muscles. Of course, you would also want strong abdominals.

Another important factor in determining the greatest development of strength is that the muscle should be exercised until it is exhausted. This exhaustion should occur at about eight repetitions of the exercise if you are working for strength. If you can do 10 repetitions, the weight is too light for maximum strength development. This is the kind of strength that a sprinter would need.

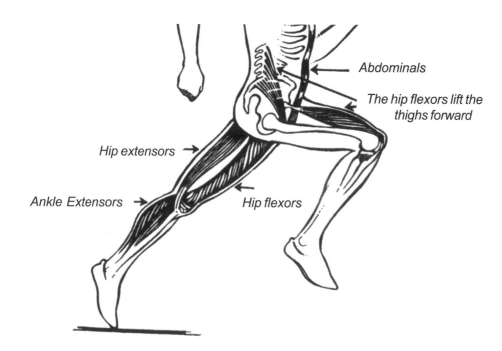

The abdominals hold the hips up so that the thighs can be lifted. If the hips drop, the stride will be shortened. The hip extensors pull the thigh backward. The ankle extensors control the toe push off.

If you are a distance runner, then working for a combination of strength and endurance would make more sense. To develop endurance in the muscle, you would exhaust your muscles after a greater number of repetitions, such as 25, 50 or more.

DO SAFE EXERCISES

Since some exercises might damage tissue, they should be avoided. The previously mentioned deep knee bend or full squat is one. If a person does a full deep knee bend, the ligaments in the front of the knee begin to be stretched after the leg has been bent more than 90 degrees. If a person continues the knee bend to the point where the calf muscles and the muscles at the back of the thigh touch, the stretching of the knee ligaments is greatly increased. So, while a deep knee bend would strengthen the muscles that extend the knee joint, they weaken the internal structure of the knee joint.

Any potentially harmful exercise that stretches the connective tissue in the abdominal area by bending too far back should be avoided. It is desirable to have tight connective tissue in the abdominal area to assist the muscles in supporting the visceral organs in the abdomen.

Another dangerous exercise is one that puts great pressure on the discs of the lower spine. The good-morning exercise, in which one bends 90 degrees at the waist and lifts a heavy weight with the lower back muscles, can put as much as 3000 to 5000 pounds of pressure per square inch on the lower spinal discs. Such pressure has ruptured the discs of some weightlifters. It can also weaken the discs and make them more susceptible to injury later in life. The amount of pressure on the discs is directly proportional to the amount of bend at the waist. So, even a dead lift, in which the bend is only about 45 degrees, could cause problems in people with weakened discs.

Pulling forward on the neck, which was common in the older style of sit ups, is also contraindicated because it might stretch the connective tissues in the back of the cervical vertebrae.

Exercises that adhere to the previous criteria — isolation of the muscle, maximum flexibility of the joint and little chance of damage to the body — are illustrated in the following exercises. Remember, as soon as you can do 10 repetitions, you can add more weight for your next workout.

Breathing effectively while exercising is important in minimizing the chance of a hernia or of rupturing blood vessels while lifting heavy weights. The best method of breathing is to exhale while lifting the weight. The second-best method is to inhale while lifting. Holding the breath is the most dangerous because the air pressure inside the chest cavity is increased when the muscles around the ribs and shoulders are contracting. This is called the *Valsalva maneuver* or Valsalva effect. The strain of the increased internal air pressure can push part of the intestine through the inguinal rings (holes) of the lower pelvic bone, causing an inguinal hernia. This is far more likely to be a problem with men than with women.

THE EXERCISES

Abdominals

Most people are aware of how important it is to have abdominal strength. It helps to keep our bellies tucked in for better posture. In fact, the abdominals, along with the lower back, are the two most important areas for strength in our bodies.

In athletics, the abdominals help to stabilize the hips, so they are essential in every action that involves the hip joints. In running and walking, the abdominals hold the hips up so that the thigh can swing through a full stride. Many runners at the international level will do 45 minutes of abdominal work daily.

Abdominal curl ups are done by lying on the floor or on a bench with the knees flexed and your hands on your chest or shoulders. (Some au-

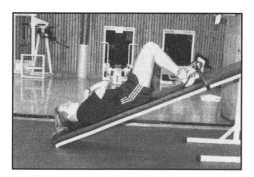 

Abdominal curl ups

thorities believe that having the hands behind the head might increase the stress on the neck area, which would be undesirable.) Curl your shoulders forward until your hips are about to leave the floor. Usually, you will be able to touch your elbows to your thighs. A normal range of motion for abdominals is less than 40 degrees.

If you do the curl ups on an inclined board with your head lower than your feet, you will also increase the resistance you are lifting. If you are working for strength, hold weight plates on your chest in order to increase resistance. But most people are looking for muscular endurance so that they can hold their tummies in longer. If this is what you want, just do many repetitions. Herschel Walker, the former professional football player, does 3500 repetitions daily.

Some people aren't sufficiently strong to do this exercise correctly the first time. If this is true for you, do the exercise this way: Grab the back of your thighs with your hands and pull yourself up to the proper position. When this becomes easy, use only one hand on one thigh to help you curl up. Soon, you will be able to do the exercise without using your hands to assist you. The exercise is easier with your hands on your hips, more difficult with your hands on your chest and most difficult with your hands on your head.

Another exercise that is often done for the abdominals is the abdominal crunch. In this exercise, you will lie flat on your back then bring your knees and shoulders upward at the same time.

Side sit ups are done to build additional strength in the muscles on the side of your abdominal area (obliques). For this exercise, most people will have to have their feet held down. (They can be hooked under a

---

CHECKLIST FOR ABDOMINAL EXERCISES

1. Flex your knees so that your hip flexors cannot contract effectively.
2. If your hips leave the bench or incline board, your hip flexors are contracting.
3. Think of yourself as *curling up* rather than *sitting up*.

Back arches using a Roman chair

barbell or a sofa.) Lift your shoulders from the mat or bench. This exercise will not only work the abdominal oblique muscles but also the muscles on one side of your lower back and the rectus abdominis on the side to which you are bending.

Lower Back

Exercises for the lower back are probably the most important for the average person to do because lower-back injuries, especially muscle pulls, are so common. The problem is that these muscles don't show up that well in our bathing suits, so we often overlook them.

The lower back muscles are essential in maintaining good posture because they are the muscles that hold our chests up by pulling our rib cages down and back. This raises the front of the rib cage and our chests. Having strong lower back muscles allows us to keep an upright posture while running or walking.

Back arches can be done on the floor. Just lie face down and raise your shoulders and knees slightly off the floor. Current thinking is that the back should not be hyperextended (greatly arched).

In a gym, there might be a Roman chair available. If so, this increases the resistance you can gain in your exercise. In a Roman chair, you will put your hips on the small saddle, hook your feet under a bar, bend forward at the waist about 30 degrees, then straighten your back.

If you desire strength, just hold weight plates or a dumbbell behind your head. If you want muscular endurance, just do as many repetitions as you can.

Hip Flexors

The hip flexors bring our thighs forward, so they are essential in any running or jumping activity. If you want to run faster, these are critical muscles to develop.

Hip flexors are exercised when the thigh is brought forward. This can be done several ways. You can do them when hanging or standing.

Hip flexors

You can do them without weights, with a weighted boot or with an ankle attachment to a pulley on a machine.

While hanging from a high bar, bring your legs forward with your knees flexed. Touch your knees to your chest.

While hanging from the high bar, alternate bringing your legs forward without bending your knees.

Using the lower pulley of a weight machine, hook your ankle into a handle or use an ankle strap to secure your ankle to the pulley. Raise your leg straight up.

While standing, with or without weight boots, brace yourself with your arms and lift one leg forward as high as it will go. Bring it up slowly.

Leg lifts are done from the supine position (on your back). Lift one or both legs from the floor to the vertical position. Your abdominals will contract isometrically in this, as they do in all other hip flexion exercises.

Knee Extensors

Extending the knee means to straighten it. The knee extensors are, therefore, used in any running or jumping activity. Some of the major knee extensor muscles also flex the hips. So, the following exercises will also strengthen your hip flexors.

On the leg extension machine, hook your feet under the padded bar. Straighten your legs. This exercise can also be done with a weighted boot.

With a partner to provide resistance, sit on a table. Let your partner

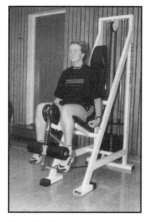

Leg Extensions

Hip extensors

put both hands on your ankle. Straighten your leg while your partner gives you just enough resistance to allow you to make the movement.

Hip Extensors

The hip extensor muscles bring the thighs from a forward position back to a straight position, such as when you are standing. They will also bring the thighs further back than straight. This is called hyperextension. The hip extensors are the muscles that supply power when you are running or jumping.

On a hip extension machine starting from a hip flexed position, extend your thigh.

With a partner, lie on your back and bring your leg up. Let your partner hold your ankle and resist as you lower your leg to the floor.

While standing and bracing yourself for balance, bring one leg backward as far as you can.

Knee Flexors (Leg Curls)

The knee flexors bend the knee. They generally work with the hip extensors, so they are useful in running. It is also essential that if the front of the thighs (the quadriceps or knee extensors) are strengthened, the knee flexors must also be strengthened.

Leg curls

On a leg extension machine, lie face down and hook your ankle under the bar. Bend your leg back at the knee joint. This exercise can also be done while standing with a weighted boot.

With a partner, lie on the floor. Let your partner supply the resistance by putting his or her hands on the back of your ankle as you flex your knee.

Ankle Plantar Flexion

Ankle plantar flexion occurs when the sole of your foot moves closer to your calf muscle. This action occurs when you rise up on your toes. This is a key area for strength and power in running and jumping.

Holding a barbell on your shoulders, rise up on your toes. This is better done with your toes on a riser board because your calf muscle will be gaining flexibility as you stretch down.

On a weight machine, with your legs straight, allow the weight to bring your ankles back, stretching your Achilles' tendon, then push the weight out with your calf muscles.

While holding a table for balance, rise up on one toe. This will give you the same resistance as holding a barbell that equals your body weight and doing the exercise with two legs. For example, if you weigh 150 pounds and hold a barbell that weighs 150 pounds, each of your calf muscles will be lifting 150 pounds. If you hold no weight but do the exercise with only one leg, the calf muscle will still be lifting 150 pounds.

By holding a dumbbell in your free hand and doing the exercise with one leg at a time, you get the same effect as adding double the amount to a barbell and doing the exercise with two legs.

Other Ankle Exercises

You can also do ankle exercises to increase dorsal flexing strength (bringing the top of your foot forward) or turning the foot inward or

 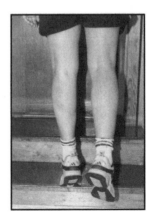

Ankle plantar flexion

Dorsal flexion

outward. There are some weight machines that do this, but these exercises are more easily done with a partner or by providing the resistance yourself.

Dorsal flexion (bringing the top of the foot closer to the front of the knee) is done by pushing down on the top of your foot with your hand, then allowing the muscles in the front of your lower leg to bring your foot upward against the resistance of your hand. This helps to prevent shin splints.

This exercise can also be done while lying on the back on a leg curl machine. Hook the toes under the pad and lift them toward your chest.

Eversion of the ankle joint occurs when you bring the outside of your foot upward. This action can be done to strengthen your ankle if you have had an ankle sprain. The damaged ligaments in a sprained ankle will take years to totally repair and shrink. But by strengthening the muscles in the outside part of your lower leg, you might be able to prevent further ankle sprains.

To do this exercise, push down in the area of your little toe and bring your foot upward and outward against the pressure of your hand.

Inversion of the ankle occurs when the sole of the foot is brought inward. This is not an action that is particularly useful. But if a person had an injury to those muscles and wanted to strengthen them, he or she would simply put a hand under the foot, applying pressure to the outside edge of the sole of the foot, then turn the foot inward against that pressure.

Arm (or Elbow) Flexion

Arm flexion occurs when you bend your elbow, decreasing the angle at the elbow. The biceps curl is the exercise that strengthens this action. The curl can be done with a barbell, a dumbbell or a set of dumbbells.

The biceps are used to hold the arms in a flexed position.

The barbell biceps curl is the most common biceps exercise. With the barbell in your hands (palms out) and your arms extended down, curl the barbell upward. The gripping of the bar will give you some isometric strength in the front of your forearms. If you want some additional

strength in the back of your forearms, you can grip the bar with your palms facing inward at the start. (This is called the reverse grip.) Alternating dumbbell curls are done by curling one dumbbell, then the other. This exercise is really just a variation of the barbell curl previously mentioned.

Since as a walker or runner you will be more interested in endurance for the muscle, you can do a larger number of repetitions with less weight — 25, 50, or 100.

Arm (or Elbow) Extension (Triceps Extension)

The triceps are used to straighten your arms. They are used in pulling your upper arm back. They are not of particular concern for recreational runners. However, if you want to do some triceps exercises, try these.

Arm flexion

The best exercise for this action is the *standing one-arm triceps extension*. The exercise being done in this position gives maximum stretch to the triceps muscle. Start with the arm holding the dumbbell extended overhead. Steady that elbow with the other hand by holding just below the elbow on the extended arm. (This stops you from cheating by allowing other muscles to come into play.) Allow the dumbbell to lower as much as possible. (This gives maximum flexibility.) Then, raise the dumbbell overhead for strength.

Biceps curl

Triceps extension

On a weight machine, use the high pulley station. Grip the bar, and with your elbows at your side, bring the bar down by straightening your arms — a triceps push-down. This exercise does not give as much flexibility as the previously mentioned exercise.

To use your own muscles to give you resistance, bend one arm and put the hand of the other arm against the wrist of the bent arm. Straighten the bent arm while resisting with the other hand.

Hip Abduction

Hip abduction means moving your leg sideways in a lateral plane. It uses the muscles on the outside of the hips. It is used by anyone who wants to move laterally while facing ahead. It is used somewhat by walkers and runners to keep their strides straight and to strengthen the muscles that come into play when moving on curves or turns.

If you have an abduction machine just sit in the seat, hook your legs into the stirrups and push both legs outward.

With a partner, lie on your back with your partner holding the outside of your feet or lower legs. Push your legs apart as far as they will go, with your partner resisting.

On a machine, use the lower pulley. While standing sideways to the machine at the low pulley station, hook your foot that is furthest from the machine into the handle (or use an ankle strap) and pull your leg away from the machine.

Hip Adduction

Hip adduction exercises strengthen the muscles on the inside of the leg (the groin area). These

Hip abduction

CHECKLIST FOR A STRENGTH WORKOUT

1. Determine the muscle groups that you want to strengthen, then select the proper exercises.
2. For strength, exhaust your muscles in six to 10 repetitions.
3. Depending on the time available, you can do one, two or three sets of the exercise. More is better.
4. For maximum effectiveness, exhaust your muscles during the exercise.
    a. If you desire strength, exhaust the muscles in less than 10 repetitions.
    b. If you desire muscular endurance, use less weight and exhaust your muscles in 20 to 100 repetitions.

Hip adduction

muscles are also used in keeping the legs striding in a straight line.

With an abduction-adduction machine, sit in the seat, put your feet in the stirrups and, with your legs apart, squeeze them together.

With a partner, start with your legs spread apart. Have your partner put his or her hands on the inside of your feet or lower legs and give you resistance as you squeeze your legs together.

On a machine with a low pulley, stand away from the machine sideways to it, with the foot nearest the machine attached to the pulley by an ankle strap and that leg abducted about 30 degrees. Squeeze your leg in toward your body, pulling the handle away from the machine.

Notes

1. Komi, P. "Neuromuscular Fatigue: Disturbed Function and Delayed Recovery After Intensive Dynamic Exercise" Keynote address at the World Congress of Sports Medicine, June 2, 1998, Orlando, FL)

2. Rasch and Morehouse 1957; Wilson, G. et al. "The specificity of strength training: the effect of posture" *European Journal of Applied Physiology*, 73 (1996): 346-352.

20
MENTAL CONSIDERATIONS

Psychologists have divided motivations into two types — those that come from within us (intrinsic motivation) and those that come from without (extrinsic motivation). If you play tennis for the fun of it, that's *intrinsic motivation*. If you play because your parents wanted you to play and gave you rewards for playing or punished you for not playing well, that's *extrinsic motivation*.

Sports psychologists have accepted these ideas and have gone a few steps further. The intrinsically motivated are those who just want to walk or run and are interested in getting better — to master the sport. They enjoy the movement and/or competition. Extrinsically motivated people, on the other hand, are interested in exercising for the health benefits — not because they enjoy the activity. They might also be interested in what others think of them — because they are fit or trim.

The intensity and extent of one's desire to accomplish any of these goals is called *motivation*. The degree of motivation can be measured by how fervently the goal or goals are pursued. It has been said that a person isn't what she says but rather what she does. So, exercising is the best proof that you enjoy the activity and what it does for you.

THE MENTAL BENEFITS OF WALKING AND RUNNING

A higher level of physical fitness helps people feel better and cope more effectively with mental stresses.[1] Their self-concept is enhanced not only by the development of a better figure but also by the feeling of success that comes from accomplishing goals that have been set.[2] Men and women who are more physically fit have better self-concepts.[3]

It is also well-known that people who exercise aerobically are happier. This seems to be a result of the release of endorphins in the brain. (Endorphins are natural brain chemicals that increase one's feeling of well-being and even euphoria.) This happens in both healthy people and in people who are clinically depressed, so walking or running is often used in mental hospitals to minimize depression.

IMAGERY

If you want to improve your technique or if you decide to enter competitions, you might want to take advantage of some mental techniques that can increase your efficiency or your reaction to competition. Imagery, or visualization, is mental practice. Much of the early work in developing the technique was done in the United States, but it was the Eastern bloc countries that refined and applied this knowledge. The basic principles, however, have been instinctively employed to some degree by many athletes for years.

In visualization, the person sees the activity from the outside or feels it from the inside. Golfer Jack Nicklaus explains the visualization process of himself as "going to the movies." He just closes his eyes and sees himself performing his swing. This is called external visualization — being on the outside and looking in. Greg Louganis, the Olympic champion diver, started his mental practice for a dive with the same kind of external visualization, but then he felt himself doing the dive. This is called internal visualization — feeling it from the inside. He also found it helpful to play appropriate music while he mentally performed the dive.

You can apply these techniques to walking or running by feeling yourself doing the activity. Check the stride, the push off, and the heel or foot plant. If you are preparing for a race, visualize each part of the race and what you should be doing. What should you do at the start? What should you do as you fatigue?

RELAXATION

Everyone can benefit from learning to relax more effectively. Hindu yogis have practiced the art of relaxation and meditation for thousands of years, and it continues to be regarded as a worthwhile pursuit today. Some years ago, a Harvard University medical doctor, Herbert Benson, developed a simple technique of relaxation in which one simply sits in a

---

CHECKLIST FOR RELAXATION

1. Sit in a quiet place.
2. Loosen your clothes.
3. Close your eyes.
4. Breathe deeply through the nose.
5. Inhibit your conscious thinking by saying a nonsense syllable (om, one, etc.) or by repeating "in" "out" as you breathe.
6. If your mind begins to think of things, don't worry. Just go back to repeating your meaningless syllables.

chair, loosens the clothes, closes the eyes and breathes deeply while shutting out extraneous thoughts.[4]

Shutting out the thoughts while breathing deeply is the key element. Benson suggests slowly repeating a nonsense syllable with each breath. You might say "one, one, one" or "om, om, om" as you inhale or exhale. Although other thoughts will come into your head, if you just keep repeating the nonsense syllable, those thoughts will leave. This type of relaxation has been shown to reduce stress and lower blood pressure.

Once you have become accomplished at the technique of relaxation, you can do it standing or sitting. In fact, many runners have learned to relax during competition. The techniques that you use relative to competition can be used effectively when you are tense at work or at school. They can also help you to get to sleep faster.

CONCENTRATION

When you concentrate, you narrow the focus of your thought power to one object or task or even just one element of an object or task. Thus, a golfer might concentrate on just one small part of the golf ball before swinging to hit it. A weight trainer might concentrate on the pressure against the hands or on one muscle group before and during the exercise. A sprinter could concentrate only on hearing the sound of the gun at the start of a race. This kind of concentration is often called *focusing*.

MENTAL TRAINING WORKS

Dr. Charles Garfield relates his experience as the subject of an experiment in the mental approach to weightlifting.[5] A weightlifter who met several Soviet psychologists at an international meeting, he doubted the validity of the results the Soviets had reported.

The Soviets asked him about his maximum bench press. He said it was 365 pounds eight years earlier when he was in serious training. They asked his most recent maximum bench press and he said 280. Then, they asked how long he thought it would take to train to again reach his maximum. He said: "At least nine months." With this information, the Soviets were ready to prove their position.

They asked him to attempt a 300-pound press. To his great surprise, he succeeded — barely. Then, they directed his relaxation using advanced techniques and had him deeply relaxed for 40 minutes. They added 65 pounds to the bar and had him visualize lifting it. They had him mentally rehearse every aspect of the lift, from the feeling in the muscles to the sounds that he made while lifting. The process was repeated until he felt totally confident in what was about to happen. He concentrated on the lift and made it — equaling his lifetime best.

This type of mental training can be applied to any walking or running competition. It can allow you to run faster because you have practiced it.

ADHERING TO YOUR EXERCISE PROGRAM

A major area of sports psychology deals with exercise adherence. As with dieting, many people start an exercise program but discontinue it after a period of time. Discount health clubs often count on this. They offer low yearly rates, collect their fees, then count on their members to drop out, leaving room for others. More legitimate health clubs want their members to stay in the program. They usually charge more in fees but continue to offer better and more effective programs.

Walk or run where you will! Do it alone or with others. Carry on conversations, listen to your Walkman or keep silent. Do it outside on the roads or trails. Do it at home or in a gym on a treadmill. Listen to music, watch TV or read while you exercise on the treadmill. The important thing is to do it:

We need to keep in mind the many positives that result from exercise

- Feeling better with more energy
- Keeping the immune system functioning at a high level, which reduces the chances for developing colds and cancers
- Keeping our HDLs (heavy density cholesterols) up and our blood pressure down, which reduce our chances of having heart attacks and strokes
- Keeping our weight controlled
- Looking better
- If there were a drug that could do what exercise does, everyone would take it every day!

REHEARSE SUCCESS

In any mental rehearsal, whether for a life goal, a weight-loss goal or a fitness goal, it is essential to think positively. Concentrating on failure will produce failure. If you concentrate on success, you are, in effect, practicing to succeed.

Notes

1. C. H. Folkins, and W. E. Sime, "Physical Fitness Training and Mental Health," *American Journal of Psychology* 36 (1981):373-389.
2. L A. Tucker, "Self-Concept A Function of Self-Perceived Somatotype," *Journal of Psychology* 113 (1983):123-133. See also Tucker, L A., "Muscular Strength and Mental Health," *Journal of Personality, Sociology, and Psychology* 45 (1983):1355-1360, and Tucker, L A.,

"Effect of Weight Training on Self Concept A Profile of Those Influenced Most," *Research Quarterly* 54 (1983):389-397.

3. J. B. Holloway, "Self-Efficacy and Training For Strength in Adolescent Girls," Master's Thesis, University of Southern California (1985).

4. Herbert Benson, *The Relaxation Response* (New York: William Morrow Company, 1975.)

5. Charles Garfield, *Peak Performance* (Los Angeles: J. B. Tarcher, 1984).